A PRACTICAL GUIDE TO ECOLOGICAL MANAGEMENT OF THE GOLF COURSE

Edited by:

R.S. Taylor, B.Sc. Hons.

Published by:

THE BRITISH AND INTERNATIONAL GOLF GREENKEEPERS
ASSOCIATION (BIGGA)
and
THE SPORTS TURF RESEARCH INSTITUTE (STRI)

First Published 1995 by:

THE BRITISH AND INTERNATIONAL GOLF GREENKEEPERS
ASSOCIATION, ALDWARK MANOR, ALDWARK, ALNE, YORK,
YO6 2NF
and
THE SPORTS TURF RESEARCH INSTITUTE, BINGLEY, WEST
YORKSHIRE, BD16 1AU, ENGLAND

ISBN: 1-873431-04-X

Photographs:
Front cover – Lindrick Golf Club
Back cover – A round with nature: a puff-ball (*Bovista plumbens*)
emulates a golf ball in the rough.

JOINT FOREWORD

I believe that this publication offers an excellent guide to golf greenkeepers on environmental and ecological management of the golf course. BIGGA has foreseen the need to be pro-active in this vital area and co-operation with the STRI has resulted in this eagerly anticipated publication. BIGGA will continue to take a lead on environmental issues and seek to work widely with all bodies who share our concerns for the future of the environment.

Mr. Neil Thomas
Executive Director, BIGGA

Golf courses are found in a wide range of situations throughout the British Isles and Continental Europe. This publication, by my colleague Mr. Robert Taylor, covers various aspects of the diversity on which golf is played. It pulls together in a practical manner a range of aspects of golf course ecological management, including woodlands, seaside links, grassland management, water features and heathlands. In addition, special habitats and specific ecological problems relating to golf are discussed.

The Sports Turf Research Institute is very pleased to work alongside the British and International Golf Greenkeepers Association in publishing this book and trusts it will remain an important source of reference for many years to come.

Dr. Peter Hayes
Director, STRI

Jacobsen E-Z-Go, a division of Textron, recognises that the turf maintenance industry has an important role to play in the management of a golf course. As a company, we ensure that our machines and the new products currently being developed meet stringent environmental and ecological considerations.

Many golf courses are constructed in areas of natural beauty and are of specific scientific interest. Therefore, people who look after golf courses are not only course managers but are also important guardians to the wildlife and habitat associated with the course. Golf course development has the potential to achieve long term conservation benefits in the countryside which include contributing to the preservation of the landscape and cultural heritage.

We are very pleased to be a major force associated with this publication.

Rene Orban
Managing Director, Jacobsen E-Z-Go UK Ltd.

ACKNOWLEDGEMENTS

This publication was jointly commissioned by the British and International Golf Greenkeepers Association (BIGGA) and The Sports Turf Research Institute (STRI), with the aim being to provide a practical source of information to the practising golf greenkeeper. I do hope that the principles within the content reach a much wider audience, including practising groundsmen working on other sports turf areas. Indeed, many of the multi-sport complexes around the country have the space and potential to practise a more pro-active form of habitat or conservation management. I sincerely hope that, as environmental legislation intensifies, greater financial incentives are forthcoming.

It is also hoped that land managers working on amenity and recreation sites and landscape architects may gain some positive practical information from this guide.

Firstly, I would like to thank both Neil Thomas and Ken Richardson of BIGGA for their continued patience throughout the period of production and for giving me the support and enthusiasm to write this publication.

I am grateful to those people who have contributed to writing sections of the book, particularly Mr. G. McKillop (Central Science Laboratories, MAFF), "Other Specific Problems"; Mr. J.W. Tucker (STRI Golf Course Architect), "An Architectural Perspective"; Mr. R. Everett (STRI Construction Consultant), "Water Features" and Dr. D.M. Lawson (STRI Soil Chemist), "Environmental Considerations in the Use of Fertilizers and Pesticides on the Golf Course". My thanks also go out to Mr. J.R. Westwood for his contribution and to Mr. D.D. Wishart (STRI Golf Course Architect), Mr. P.M. Canaway (Assistant Director – Research, STRI), Dr. P. Hayes (STRI Director), Mr. D.F. Boocock (STRI Senior Agronomist) and Mr. R.D.C. Evans (STRI Agronomist) for reviewing sections, proof-reading and for their constructive comments throughout.

Finally, my sincere thanks must go to Mrs. Ann Bentley for her considerable speed, skill and professionalism on the desktop publishing system and in transforming my rather spider-like scrawl into the finished form. Her enthusiasm and patience are virtues to be cherished.

R.S. TAYLOR
STRI, Bingley   **MAY 1995**

CONTENTS

PART 1

SETTING THE SCENE

1.1 INTRODUCTION

Concern about the environment continues to grow as more and more land is taken and fragmented through habitat modification and destruction. In the world of golf, concern continues to intensify as more new facilities are placed within a diminishing countryside resource.

Although at the time of writing the golf development boom has stabilised somewhat, the industry is becoming gripped and, to some extent, strangled by the increasing number of regulations governing future development. Indeed, one has only to look into Europe to see the effects of such broad-scale restrictions on both development and golf course (turf) management. This must therefore pose the question, "Are golf courses really that bad for the environment?" I suspect not; but the answer is not so clear cut. Thought given to the initial layout in relation to the site together with the way in which individual courses are managed are of fundamental importance. Should the layout be architecturally weak, possibly in relation to the "natural" featuring of the site or its topography and vegetation, then almost all management treatments aimed at improving environmental quality or indeed the playing characteristics will be of little benefit.

It is imperative therefore that at the outset the golf course architect is sufficiently competent and skilled in being able to create a layout which draws upon all the site has to offer, satisfying the stringent requirements of the game for both tiger and moderate player, with sufficient thought given to the positioning of each hole so as to take into account the potential and nature of the habitat types present. Integral with this would be the recognition of the objectives for their future management.

It is largely what has become termed over-manicuring or, conversely, management neglect that is generating increasing environmental concern from conservation bodies, non-statutory and governmental organisations and indeed the general public. It is often the case that on the golf course areas are left without management so as to "benefit the wildlife". These areas can quite often lose their ecological diversity and environmental appeal, resulting in an untidy rough vegetation community consisting of far fewer desired species than originally present. A good example here would be the grasslands which, if managed, will continue to support a moderate botanical diversity. If neglected, competition from invading weedgrasses may alter the overall sward composition, allowing complete dominance of just one or two species. Normally, the next stage on the golf course would be the increasing criticism from members and the removal and "over-management" of the area.

Although it is without question the roughs that offer the greatest potential for ecological management, we should not lose sight of the importance of the more intensively managed areas such as the semi-roughs and fairways, all of which constitute the "through the greens". These areas are important as vantage points and feeding areas and they also indirectly serve to increase the area of marginal habitat, so raising further the overall ecological potential.

PLATE 1. The fairway and semi-rough can provide important ecological linking through the course.

With the continuing diminution of our countryside, wildlife and conservation groups have recognised the problems regarding land destruction and modification and have attempted to safeguard areas of ecological significance through their purchase and protection. Nature reserves, although of considerable value, will never be sufficiently numerous or extensive to guarantee the survival of more than a limited fraction of our animal/plant communities. The value of nature reserves therefore lies in their contribution to and relationship with the surrounding land which harbours a variety of natural and semi-natural vegetation types. Thus, the roadside verges, railway embankments and indeed the golf course are becoming increasingly important as marginal habitats and unofficial nature reserves. Indeed, many of the more traditional golf courses are often guardians of some very important nationally and internationally recognised habitat and species types of major conservation, or ecological, value. Many others are set within important scenic areas and are therefore important aspects of our historic and archaeological heritage.

1.2 BACKGROUND

Historical Perspective

To appreciate the needs and objectives of ecological management it is important to have a basic understanding of the history of the countryside and the processes involved in its formation.

Great Britain throughout its history has undergone many changes, of which geology and climate have been the prime movers. These linked together have given structure to the great diversity of the British landscape. One cannot, however, overlook the massive influence that generations of mankind have added, either positively or negatively, to this diversity. Probably the most creative human force in shaping the landscape as we see it today has been the introduction of farming from around 5000 BC with its associated felling of vast hectares of wildwood followed by man's increase in population size from 20,000 inhabitants which existed in Neolithic times to the 60,000,000 existing today.

Almost all of the landscape following the last Ice Age some 8000 years BC became wooded, originally with birch moving gradually into Southern Britain from Europe as the ice retreated and the climate ameliorated. A second sweep of birch was to invade from the North to almost totally cover the British landscape. Birch was and still is a pioneer, "setting the scene" creating the woodland conditions for the gradual spread of other longer-lived tree species. Pine, like birch, was represented quite early in the formation of the first wildwoods, particularly through the South and South East of the country, later appearing and spreading through the North East. Hazel gradually increased in importance, colonising originally from the North and West.

By the Atlantic period some 7000 to 5000 years BC pine had dominated the far North and the South East, including East Anglia. Thermophilous (warm loving) trees such as lime began to take advantage of the birch woodland. Elm reached its peak before entering into an unexplained decline, allowing oak to equal and exceed the elm. Oak continued to increase throughout the country with hazel dominating the understorey. The gradual spread of oak eventually excluded much of the pioneer woodland, except in Caledonia where pine persisted.

During the Atlantic period the total forest cover reached its maximum. Oak (and possibly lime in local areas) dominated, with elm, birch, alder, ash, beech and willow being represented. Associated understorey trees and shrubs would include hazel, field maple, holly, ivy, rowan and aspen.

Forest clearance began during the Mesolithic period (4500 BC), increasing substantially during the Neolithic and Bronze Age periods.

These early farmers developed a policy of shifting agriculture, clearing areas of forest only to move as the fertility of the land waned. Man's influence was at first slow, allowing sufficient time for wildlife which had followed the progress of the woodlands to exploit the developing mosaic of habitats being created. Within 2000 years large areas of the country were converted to farmland and heath. Much of the wildwood at higher altitudes and through the river valleys was to disappear. Indeed, it has been said that half of England had ceased to be wildwood by the Iron Age (600 BC).

It was during the Iron Age that settlements and villages were to develop, with cattle, goats and sheep helping to retain the habitat mosaic and suppress the processes of succession that restore the woodland condition.

Thus, with the improved tools of the day, deforestation continued. Wildlife was not just having to adapt rapidly to the new environments being created but was also having to be flexible with respect to habitat preference (they needed a great resilience in order to survive).

Many species – a good example being the skylark – were successful in moving out of the diminishing woodlands into the newly found open habitats. Today, the skylark is becoming much rarer within the countryside as the speed of change through habitat modification and/or destruction continues and is simply too fast for further adaptation.

Mankind has had dominance over the formation of the landscape and it is now our duty to continue with appropriate management/ conservation policies and strategies to ensure the future survival of the great wealth and diversity of species which have come to be so dependent upon it.

1.3 THE GOLF COURSE RESOURCE

The modern landscape ranges from the elevated oligotrophic (nutrient-poor) bogs and mires to the southern heathlands of Dorset, Sussex and East Anglia. From acidic to basic grasslands, the woodlands and the sand dunes and the maritime environments around our coastline. Interestingly, all of these habitat types can be found, often strongly represented, on golf courses.

It was the gradual exhaustion of the favoured link and heathland sites that encouraged further development on moorland and the heavier soils of the parklands. In more recent years, courses have been constructed on a wide range of soil types, with particular emphasis being given to farmland and reclaimed land..

Although the older golf courses built upon the "favoured" land are, with positive management, helping to safeguard some nationally and internationally important sites, the newly constructed courses on otherwise sterile land offer an opportunity to create sympathetic habitats within the site. Thus, with forethought these courses can contribute to conservation. Much, however, depends at the outset on the close liaison between the competent and recognised golf course architect and the golf course ecologist.

There are in the region of 2500 golf courses now established throughout Great Britain. Many of these are in prime positions with regard to their ecological significance. The total land area occupied by golf may today (1995) be estimated at around 150,000 hectares with up to 50,000 hectares being designated as rough, much of which is given very little management. Golf therefore does represent a major land use.

From the ecological viewpoint, it is not just the vast hectareage occupied by golf or the conservation of important habitat types but, if developed and managed with sensitivity and in sympathy with the natural vegetation, topography and other landform characteristics, the golf course can play a very important role in providing unofficial nature reserves of substantial habitat diversity and interest. Like the country's roadside verges and railway embankments, golf courses can act as ecological corridors through which wildlife can move and extend their range of spatial distribution. Such marginal linking systems play a vital role in the countryside in helping species otherwise restricted to a given area to evacuate should the land become unstable or further modified. Indeed, many weak-flying or wingless insects, for example, may be totally dependent upon such land bridges. This concept is being further extended in parts of Europe where areas of carry or rough grassland are being created as bands running across the fairways at intervals through the golf course so facilitating the "safe" passage across as well as along the course.

Nationally, golf courses support many rare and uncommon species and vegetation types. Dawlish Warren golf course in Devon is a Site of Special Scientific Interest (SSSI) and is the only site on mainland Britain for the Warren crocus (*Romulea columnae*); a Gloucestershire golf course is a Site of Nature Conservation Importance (SNCI) with a rich flora containing many thousands of green-winged orchids (*Orchis morio*); Therfield Heath golf course in Hertfordshire is part of a Local Nature Reserve (LNR) and is one of the best sites for the threatened pasque flower (*Pulsatilla vulgaris*); Kent golf courses support the lesser and clove-scented broomrapes (*Orobanche minor* and *O. caryophyllacea*) amongst a number of other interesting plants; Luffenham Heath golf course in Leicestershire is an SSSI containing a rich limestone grassland flora, badgers and nightingales; Woodhall Spa - another SSSI - and Linwood golf courses in Lincolnshire have colonies of marsh gentian (*Gentiana pneumonanthe*). The Royal Birkdale in Southport is home to Britain's rarest amphibian, the natterjack toad (*Bufo calamita*) and to another nationally endangered creature, the sand lizard (*Lacerta agilis*). Many other courses support flora and fauna of lesser rarity which benefit from no official protection but are nevertheless important marginal ecosystems. Such species tend to survive largely through the greenkeeper's benign neglect although intensification of management is putting them at risk.

M. FORDHAM, *Journal of the Sports Turf Res. Inst.* (1988)

Although it is without question the roughs that offer the greatest potential for ecological management, we should not lose sight of the importance of the more intensively managed areas such as the semi-roughs, the carry and fairway, all of which will vary between courses depending upon their position and vegetation type. These areas provide important vantage or look-out posts as well as feeding sites. They also serve very importantly in increasing the overall edge effect, thus effectively increasing their potential ecological/conservation significance.

Disadvantages
Much of what has been discussed so far has been positively encouraging and does serve to illustrate that golf and nature can coexist and together can contribute significantly to nature conservation. There are, however, real criticisms levelled at the golf industry.

PLATE 2. Inappropriate landscaping and management can generate public concern.

Working in the golf industry, we constantly hear of the threat of environmental damage and social upheaval caused by the international golf boom. Indeed, the golf boom in Britain has provoked strong protest by the Council for the Protection of Rural England (CPRE) which argues that golf is often a camouflage towards suburbanisation of the countryside. Similarly, we constantly hear of the "Augusta dream", so named after the famous course in Georgia and consisting of wide fertilizer enriched fairways and narrow, closely cropped bands of rough. Such courses do not blend with the British landscape but will transform it, possibly involving considerable civil engineering skill and the obliteration of many intrinsic features of the site, including its vegetation. Clearly, inappropriate construction techniques, the over-use of chemicals, i.e. fertilizers and pesticides, and the over-management of roughs will not only generate opposition but will create a sterile, featureless course largely inimitable to wildlife, offering very little thought towards the improvement of ones game.

Objections
The principal objections therefore facing the golf industry include:

• Altered land use
• Golf-related tourism
• Inappropriate landscaping
• Management – neglect or ignorance

14

Altered Land Use
Altered land use or the destruction of one habitat to provide a second of lower ecological value is a major area of contention and one which must be fully addressed from the outset by way of a detailed ecological appraisal and architectural feasibility study outlining appropriate development guidelines.

Recreating the Augusta dream in areas of high ecological significance would be clearly unacceptable, but sympathetic design using all of what the site has to offer to create a more traditional British course may be acceptable providing that continued support with respect to its management is given, i.e. no preventative usage of pesticides and minimal use of fertilizers on immediate putting surfaces.

Golf-Related Tourism
Golf-related tourism is by far the greatest environmental concern and one which CPRE has been quick to condemn. Here, we are not talking of a single 18 hole golf course on arable land, but a whole complex, possibly comprising of an 18 hole course, 9 hole par 3, driving range and an array of associated developments such as hotel complexes and fairway housing bringing increased traffic and tourism into an otherwise heavily rural area of the countryside.

The gradual suburbanisation of the countryside clearly governed by monetary power is doing much to harm the traditional concept of the game.

The scale of the development must be constrained by the overall sensitivity of the site and this can only be determined following a full ecological appraisal and possibly (if required) an environmental impact assessment.

Generally speaking, a golf course clubhouse and car park built within sufficient land (preferably 60-90 hectares) and in the absence of other negative factors should provide space for suitable wildlife refuges.

Larger scale facilities such as hotels or residential developments will need to be considered in the context of the local planning guidelines. Indeed, the potential environmental sensitivity of the site may be such so as to make the combined development unacceptable. This indeed could be on the grounds of increased traffic generation or increased water abstraction which the ancillary development may bring.

Inappropriate Landscaping
Inappropriate landscaping may include both the larger scale alterations

to the land via what is known as hard landscaping involving massive scale earth movement in order to create the hills, valleys, nuances and other topographical features and the soft landscaping approach of using trees, often inappropriate, and other vegetation to create a desired landscape.

The well informed architect will use his skill and expertise to fit the golf course into the landscape using all that the given site has to offer. Indeed, most sites assessed by the Sports Turf Research Institute (STRI) have intrinsic featuring which can be used to add flair and interest to the potential golf course design.

It is often the golf professional or other outside development company disregarding or eliminating the advice of the architect who is at the forefront of the controversy over hard landscaping techniques. This unnecessary approach does generate considerable opposition from both the statutory and non-statutory bodies, including the general public.

Similarly, with soft landscaping, a careful approach should be given to the most appropriate vegetation types for any particular site. Full use should be made of an ecological appraisal to ascertain the principal habitat types, retaining, extending and/or maintaining these during the development period.

On the mature or established course, criticism is often voiced over the straight line regimentations of one tree type separating fairways or to the few small clumps of trees forming insignificant, almost artificial copses. Concern may also be expressed as to the use of totally inappropriate, alien or exotic species planted within the roughs, often compromising ecologically sensitive habitat types. Such landscaping does very little to improve the playing of the game and even less towards enhancing the environment.

Management – Neglect or Ignorance
Although the majority of greenkeepers tend to have a good basic knowledge of fine turf management, relatively few have spent time studying applied ecological management. Indeed, it is only over the last few years (1991–1994) that ecological considerations have been thought important enough to be included in the National/Scottish Vocational Qualifications (N/SVQ). Even less expertise is available at the golf club committee level, but it is often the whim of the changing committees that dictates whether rough management work is worthy of special consideration. A more sympathetic approach to ecological management will do much to reduce the public concern.

PLATE 3. Loss of aesthetic and ecological appeal through inappropriate landscaping.

Management of the roughs will necessitate a basic understanding of the variety of habitat types and the requirements of the very different management approaches available to the greenkeeper.

1.4 ARCHITECTURAL PERSPECTIVE

There has been little original thinking in golf course architecture since the days of H.S. Colt, Dr. A. MacKenzie and T. Simpson in the 1920s and 1930s. Their approach could be regarded as traditional as they attempted (and usually succeeded) in applying the principle of using all the site had to offer. Their's was the "genius loci" (genius of the place) and by minimising transformation of the land they created, or rather retained, a natural landscape which harmonised with the surroundings.

The architects of the golden era of the 1920s and 30s did not shun earth movement altogether as, where land was deficient, they painstakingly produced features which echoed the shaping forces of nature.

However, transformation of the landscape to suit the architect was only feasible with the introduction of large earth moving equipment – initially the steam shovel and bulldozer: more recently the giant motor scraper.

The approach of sculpting golf courses from the landscape was initially pioneered in the United States of America. It can be defined as an imposed style of architecture unrelated to its surroundings. Natural features or subtleties of the site are largely ignored or built over due to inexperience, laziness or arrogance.

There has been a reaction to the imposed architectural approach in more recent years and a swing back to a more traditional form of architecture. Low profile architecture has been re-established in the USA which was practised 80 years before, when courses were designed to fit the land. The success of this less extravagant approach is limited by the raw materials on which the architect has to work. Endowed with its rolling links, early designers had to seek out the best features for the elements of golf. Great skill is needed to recreate these features of natural dune land without intimating the hand of man.

Given the dwindling number of good sites and increasing number of bland sites, the architect is severely tested. In these situations, there is a call for greater earth movement to create landscape and playing interest. In urban or suburban areas, golf courses provide welcome relief from housing and industry which press up against the boundaries and provide a buffer against further development. By implication, the architectural approach will essentially be imposed in these situations to foster the feeling of isolation within the more pleasant environment of the golf course. In rural situations, the golf course needs to be integrated with its surroundings.

There may be no lovely heathlands or true links sites available for development but through sensitive design there is greater chance of developing the better sites and thereby providing a golf course which will succeed in the long term. This may call for the introduction of native trees and shrubs, together with conservative ground shaping to form swales, depressions and subtle mounding in preference to bunkers; greens and tees to be constructed as inconspicuously as possible and fairways contoured and narrowed by graduating the rough.

A bolder approach may well be justified where the surrounding landscape is rugged and changes in elevation more abrupt. Conversely, a links style of architecture imposed on a flat site would appear completely out of context and a sculpted look with gentle contours and well rounded features more in keeping.

A feeling for nature and ability to echo this in the landscaping of the golf course is more important that copying or introducing new gimmicks.

PLATE 4. A golf green fitted into the landscape.

Agricultural sites account for most new golf course developments and where these are comparatively featureless there is greater freedom for the golf course architect to exercise his imagination without over-exaggeration. Thorough site investigation is still essential to minimise potential conflict with hedges, ancient site boundaries (possibly marked by sunken lanes and raised banks), remnant ancient woodland and topographical features of historical significance.

Although a smaller percentage of planning applications are linked with historic buildings and parks, this is one aspect which must be sympathetically handled. By seeking out the best routine for the holes and natural green and tee positions, the need for remodelling of the landscape is minimised. The historic core of the property can remain untouched or tees/greens placed sufficiently far away to avoid intrusion.

The furniture of the golf course, e.g. tee markers, seats, signposts, paths, steps and maintenance facilities, have a major visual impact. In sensitive areas, this needs to be minimised by reducing their occurrence and, secondly, using appropriate materials.

The support facilities for the golf course can also have a most damaging effect on the landscape. This can be mitigated by shielding access roads and placing the clubhouse at a lower elevation or possibly within a natural woodland clearing.

Trees are a major design element along with sand and water as they help to provide definition, reinforce golfing strategy and provide a pleasant backdrop. Existing woodland can be successfully integrated, ensuring that tree preservation orders are respected. New plantings need to reinforce the intentions of the architect as well as being in keeping with the balance of native species. It is important to remember that trees have a finite lifespan, therefore where feature trees are the key to playing strategy of a hole, there must be a plan of replacement.

Exotic plants around the clubhouse may provide a pleasant immediate setting but further out on the course look more like a garden centre than a natural part of the landscape. The abundance of silver birch and cupressus produce a monotonous backdrop on many of our inland courses despite their advantages of rapid establishment and growth. The incorporation of native, longer lived trees (within the general planting framework) gives the impression of the golf course growing into the surrounding countryside and adds variety to the overall scheme.

Unfortunately, tree planting is often considered a personal means of leaving a mark on the golf course without regard for the implications. As a result, the original intentions of the architect may be destroyed or panoramic vistas blocked. Golfers seem to prefer the seclusion of dense, tree-lined fairways as if golf is a subversive activity to be shielded from prying eyes. This creates an unnatural impression due to the abrupt change from woodland to fairway and places an additional barrier between the public and the golf course.

Water features have become a signature of many American style courses with subsequent importation into other countries. Undoubtedly, water provides an immediate visual impact, serves irrigation purposes and provides a major challenge (or threat) to the golfer. This may satisfy the environmentalists, who applaud conservation of water (and associated habitat), but it can have a significant impact on the landscape if over-worked. When tied in with regular rolling mounds and hollows, together with large jigsaw-type bunkers (filled with dazzling white sand), the appearance is usually completely alien to the natural surroundings.

Reducing acreages available for golf course development have served to squeeze layouts. The concentration of holes has increased their visual impact and diminished their conservation role. There must be space for additional planting and preservation of existing habitats.

Running parallel to this phenomenon has been the pressure for longer golf courses, mainly in response to improvements in golfing equipment. By attempting to force excessively long holes into small acreages, the scope for providing an environmentally-rich golf course, with room for plants and animals, is greatly reduced. Furthermore, the latitude for introducing strategic elements into play is also limited by long parallel holes with little separation.

It is the architect's responsibility, working in conjunction with the golf course ecologist, to say if a golf course can be successfully fitted into the land without damaging the landscape, its visual appeal or conservation value. By defining the constraints or potential of a site at an early stage, an optimum design solution can be derived.

In conclusion, many of our golf courses are simply well manicured parks with naturalness suppressed in the interests of order and demands of play. We have also been conditioned by the image of a small percentage of golf courses brought to their peak of perfection for major competitions. We need to strip away some of the frills and window-dressing to reveal the true substance of the golf course.

Uniformity is the overriding threat to the future of our countryside and golf provides an opportunity to break up the monotony. There is room for expression in golf course architecture, but in an attempt to create this artificially, through massive earth movement, there is the risk of courses becoming monotonous and of a single landscape type dedicated entirely to the image of golf. The elements of the golf course must harmonise and directly relate to the surroundings.

Economics alone may enforce an eventual return to the traditional form of golf course architecture, but this process should be encouraged by architects who appreciate and can demonstrate the link between nature and golf.

1.5 THROUGH THE GREEN MANAGEMENT

Management Plan

An essential starting point for sound environmental management must at the outset be to devise a management plan for the course. This could be done in-house, providng that the Head Greenkeeper/Course Manager has sufficient competence to the level now being required by the Greenkeepers Training Committee (GTC) (see Appendix II) or by a competent and recognised golf course ecologist who will build into the plan the strategic and aesthetic parameters as considered important for the course.

The plan must outline a structured, phased timetable of works, possibly extending over 5 to 15 years – it is indeed rarely practical or feasible to carry out the bulk of the work in just one or two years. Finances and labour resources within the club must be considered; labour, i.e. the greenstaff, should have more spare capacity during the winter period and this can therefore be accommodated in the plan.

Undertaking the work on a phased basis, i.e. annually, working discrete areas at any one time is likely to be ecologically sensible, helping to create areas of increased structural diversity, i.e. height, density and form, etc., so offering a greater range of habitat types for species colonisation.

The management plan could form part of an ongoing policy document, ideally drawn up by the Course Manager/Head Greenkeeper and Secretary using information gathered from the independent ecological/ management appraisal undertaken on behalf of the club. A management representative, usually the Head Greenkeeper, should be responsible for updating the document in regard to improved practices or changes in external constraints. Close liaison between the club's liaison officer, greenkeeper, green chairman and the ecologist will remain an essential component of the ongoing programme.

The document should identify the principal habitat types and give a full description of the ecology of the course. The initial site inspection should be used to help the club formulate management objectives, the options available, together with an outline or series of prescriptions of the management works necessary.

If the above is carried out, it should be possible to administer an annual works programme which can then be monitored by way of a site management record. Recording and monitoring the progress being made will help in the understanding of the effects of the management works, both on the wildlife and acceptance or non-acceptance to club members. This obviously will be of particular relevance to the longer term ongoing projects, especially to those clubs with regularly changing committees.

How successful would an ecological appraisal and management programme actually be to our club?
It should be possible to answer the above with just two examples immediately coming to mind from the numerous clubs now benefiting from the Ecological Management Service run by the STRI.

The first concerns Temple Golf Club, Hurley, Berkshire. Temple Golf Club commissioned an ecological appraisal of the course in 1990. As a result of the recommendations given, some significant changes were made to the management techniques. Emphasis was given to the cutting regimes employed through the grassland roughs, together with woodland management, i.e. thinning, restocking and understorey

PLATE 5. The grassland roughs – Temple Golf Club.

regeneration. The original grasslands were noted to be of significant ecological value but possibly were not expressing themselves botanically due to the cutting regimes in place. An amendment to the cutting of the semi-roughs, carries and roughs and thinning works around the woodland margins has revealed some very interesting results.

The roughs rather than being neglected are now cut twice a year, in spring and late summer, with cuttings being removed to prevent nutrient enrichment which does tend to encourage vigorous weedgrasses at the expense of the wild flowers. The semi-roughs are cut weekly to three weekly depending upon position and growing conditions. These two areas alone have been found to be particularly species rich. Indeed, a site report commissioned by the Berkshire, Buckinghamshire and Oxfordshire Naturalist Trust (BBONT) and Windsor and Maidenhead Wildlife Group (WMWG) revealed over 200 species of flowering plant, including a very large colony of green winged orchids estimated at over 200 plants. Bee and pyrimidal orchids are also increasing. It is claimed that on the basis of the orchids alone, Temple merits scheduling as a Site of Special Scientific Interest. Helleborines, spurge laurel and wood spurge have now been recorded within the woodland margins. Badger setts and badger tracks were also found within the woodland margins and evidence of their foraging noted within the semi-roughs. This list goes on!

The second example concerns a golf club in West Germany, Golf Club Hösel, who were anticipating building a second 18 hole course within arable land adjacent the existing golf facility. The club met with strong environmental opposition and consequently commissioned the STRI to carry out an ecological appraisal of the new land and the established course.

It soon became obvious that very little attention was being given to management of through the greens. Little wonder therefore that opposition to the project was so strong. Recommendations were made to improve the ecology of the established course through tree planting and relaxation of cutting heights within the roughs. In 1993, the STRI was invited to attend the club and to take part in the presentation of an Environmental Award. This, through the German Golf Federation and the Local Statutory Authorities, was given in recognition of the excellent ecological results achieved by the club and it does show that with guidance great strides can be made with respect to improving the ecological significance of the golf course whilst improving relations with those authorities keen to implement developmental restrictions.

1.6 OBJECTIVES OF MANAGEMENT

Ecological

[a] To ensure that the management prescriptions carried out on the golf course are both **practical** and **sustainable**.
Many species of wildlife will become increasingly dependent upon the habitat types created, necessitating that the management programme be both practical with respect to its implementation and sustainable or continuous into the longer term.

[b] To **develop and maintain diversity** within the habitat.
Diversity can be used to describe the structural variation of a given habitat, of which will include density, variation in height, age and species. In a wild flower grassland for example, the principal objective may be to encourage species diversity, whilst on the heathland habitat developing diversity of species may not be the principal objective. Here, variation in height, growth form and age may be more important. It can be seen therefore that the concept of diversity will be habitat-dependent and is therefore referred to as appropriate in the following sections.

[c] To develop an ongoing **timing of works** so as to minimise ecological disruption when carrying out any management operation.

[d] To give regard to the **careful and considerate execution of works**, with particular emphasis being given to phasing of work, the careful use of herbicides (if necessary), the types of machinery used and the manner of their use.

[e] To create an appropriate **balance** between the varying habitat types within the landscape, i.e. woodlands, grasslands, water features, etc.

Golf

[a] To maintain an **adequate throughput** of traffic around the course.

[b] To facilitate **continuous play** in and out of the rough areas.

[c] To retain and improve the **strategy** of each hole.

[d] To retain the aesthetic and **visual quality** both on and off the course.

PART 2

THE HABITAT

2.1 HEATHLAND/MOORLAND

Rationale for Management

Preserving the "natural" heathland/moorland character must remain one of our primary objectives. If the above is true then we must at the outset determine what the natural character should be and we can only establish this by first defining just what we mean by heathland and moorland. Heathland forms a characteristic open landscape, generally occurring on nutrient-poor acid soils. In the strict sense, they are plant communities dominated by shrubs of the heather family, of which ling (*Calluna vulgaris*) is the commonest. Although heather is by definition the characteristic dominant vegetation, we can extend this definition as appropriate to golf to include the areas of gorse, bracken and the varying types of acidic, basic and alkaline grasslands. Many of the heathlands on golf courses tend to be, at least in part, supporting mixed scrub/ woodland communities which in many respects can be classed as weeds within the principal habitat type.

In Britain, the heather-dominated heathlands and moorlands represent a substantial proportion of the total world resource. Being confined by their restricted geographical distribution, heathlands are of particular conservation importance. These areas, generally nutrient-poor, can support many very rare or localised plant species and do invariably help in the conservation of internationally important bird and insect populations.

Today the heathlands are extremely fragmented and although restricted by natural processes, i.e. geology and climate both of which influence their formation; major losses, including continued intensification of farming practices, housing, industry and forestry, have over the past century been quite severe. These combined have severely reduced the heathland resource with the largest remaining areas being concentrated through the South and South East of England, Norfolk (particularly the brecklands), Devon and Cornwall, together with a few remnants in the West Midlands and the Pennines of Derbyshire through to West Yorkshire. A few remaining fragments of heathland can be found through South Yorkshire and into North Yorkshire.

Heathlands, although exhibiting an air of "naturalness", are a product of human activity and the processes of early deforestation and will if left unmanaged quickly revert back to their original state. It is therefore important to accept from the outset that the existence of our heathlands is purely a result of the complex interactions between the vegetation types and the effect of their management. Management may be natural, i.e. through fire, storm damage, etc. and herbivorous grazing from rabbits or other rodents, or through the intentional practices of burning, grazing or cutting.

Lowland heathlands are by their composition inherently unstable with successional change normally being quite rapid following the cessation of management. Upland heathlands, i.e. the moorlands, with their podzolic soil types characterised by a varying layer of peat, i.e. from several inches to several feet thick, are much more stable and are therefore less prone to successional change. Indeed, with the constant high rainfall levels, mineral leaching may be high leaving the soil profile very infertile, thus restricting natural tree regeneration.

The Soil Profile

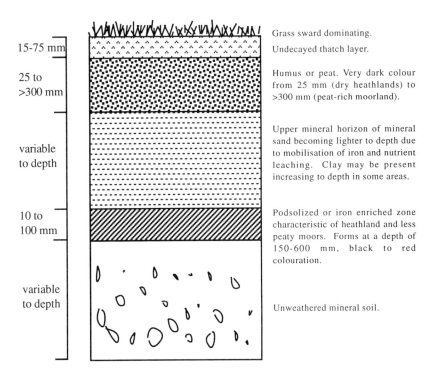

15-75 mm — Grass sward dominating. Undecayed thatch layer.

25 to >300 mm — Humus or peat. Very dark colour from 25 mm (dry heathlands) to >300 mm (peat-rich moorland).

variable to depth — Upper mineral horizon of mineral sand becoming lighter to depth due to mobilisation of iron and nutrient leaching. Clay may be present increasing to depth in some areas.

10 to 100 mm — Podsolized or iron enriched zone characteristic of heathland and less peaty moors. Forms at a depth of 150-600 mm, black to red colouration.

variable to depth — Unweathered mineral soil.

The characteristic heathland soil profile may or may not comprise a surface thatch layer. Certainly in heather-dominated areas this layer may be totally missing, often being replaced with a superficial trash layer of undecayed heather material with *Sphagnum* or other mosses, all of which, like thatch, will inhibit seed germination from the buried seed bank which is normally present within the second layer, i.e. the humus or peat layer. This dark organic-rich layer may be quite variable in depth, extending to around 25-50 mm in the sandy, dry lowland heathlands to much deeper in the peat-rich moorlands. This layer forms the main rooting zone of the heather plants and may contain a considerable bank of buried viable seeds of heather and these may possibly remain viable for many years. It may be that the bulk of the seed will be concentrated within the top 20-25 mm, reducing rapidly thereafter. The humus layer normally gives way quite sharply to a mineral sand layer of variable depth which often displays a gradation in colour, normally being light brown within the vicinity of the humus layer, becoming progressively more bleached at depth due to the mobilisation of iron, aluminium, etc. percolating down through the profile. The sand band normally gives way to a hard black layer called a humus pan which lies immediately above a rust-coloured iron-rich podzol, both of which are formed due to the percolation of rainwater and deposition of the iron compounds, whereupon they cement the soil particles together to form the characteristic pan. The podzol can be quite inhibitory to the penetration of tree and indeed heather roots.

The pH value of most heathland soils will vary between 3.5 and 5.5 and the optimum level for the germination of heather seed would be in the order of 4.0 to 4.5. The soils are generally very deficient in phosphorus, nitrogen and indeed total levels of exchangeable cations. The drier alkaline heathlands supporting a base-rich mineral soil type may support a relatively patchy and often quite superficial layer of acidic sand upon which the *Calluna* can develop around an otherwise quite alkaline grassland community.

Management Problems
The principal management problems on the heathland golf course are normally attributable to management neglect or ignorance and can be summarised as outlined below:

(a) *Succession*
Gradual loss of habitat quality via the natural invasion of tree species.

Gradual loss of habitat quality via the invasion of grasses.

Both the above will be exacerbated by management neglect or ignorance.

(b) *Management neglect/ignorance*
Quality of habitat deteriorates as heather becomes old, leggy and degenerate (invasion of grasses and trees likely).

Management Limitations
[a]   Heather is sensitive to damage through trampling by golfers, vehicular damage and the likely disturbance through tree clearance all of which can weaken and possibly kill localised areas, allowing weedgrasses to invade and proliferate.

[b]   The natural vegetative regeneration capacity is seriously reduced (by 90%) in older mature to degenerate heather.

[c]   Certain management treatments are inappropriate and will leave woody stems, litter, etc. which will affect play.

Management Prescription
Natural Tree/Shrub Regeneration and Its Control
On the heathland course the presence of trees such as pine (*Pinus sylvestris*) or birch (*Betula* sp.) in moderation may be an asset as both provide important invertebrate habitats and are used by birds. Both these species, however, are vigorous colonists which, once established, become increasingly difficult to remove. If left, they may seriously compromise the ecological significance of the course, of which heather is normally dominant, and may seriously alter the course character with respect to playing quality, i.e. with loss of sight lines and heather dominated hazards. It is therefore vital that written into the course management programme (policy document) is an item covering the annual clearance of invading trees and shrubs from the heather dominated areas of the course. Over the first few years of setting up a

PLATE 6. Naturally regenerating pine and birch will reduce the ecological significance of the heathland habitat.

31

management programme removal will need to concentrate on larger trees. These can be physically grubbed out but this will undoubtedly create substantial damage to the underlying heather sward, possibly with considerable disturbance to the soil profile and dilution of the surface seed bank.

Cutting may be a preferred option but unsightly stumps could create further problems for ball retrieval, physical injury, vegetative regrowth and may seriously restrict mechanical treatments engaged in maintenance of the heather sward. To reduce these problems, stumps should be ground below surface level and all cut material removed from the site to prevent nutrients building up in the soil.

In those areas where much of the heathland character has been lost due to tree invasion, the surface should be scraped or heavily scarified so as to re-expose the underlying humus and the viable heather seed bank. If the area has been wooded for over 50 years, then reseeding using cut heather material may be necessary.

Grass Invasion and Its Suppression
Grass encroachment in and amongst the heather sward with time can result in the formation of a considerable band of fibrous thatch above the surface humus, which may restrict light penetration and germination of the heather seed. Indeed, often noted on golf courses is the rapid growth of heather in divot scars created during play on fairways adjacent heather dominated roughs.

PLATE 7. Grass invasion and the gradual loss of heather.

32

Although on the fairways fibre may only develop to around 20 mm depth, it may in the deeper roughs extend to depths exceeding 75 mm (3 in.). Its removal therefore can represent a considerable problem. Weedkilling alone using selective herbicides although inhibiting the growth of the competing grasses will not help in assisting the germination of heather. The first priority therefore must be to look at methods effective in its removal.

(1) *Sod cutting*. Sod cutting using a turf sod cutter, possibly undertaking two passes, may indeed be an appropriate technique. It is, however, quite laborious and is only recommended for small areas. It will be important that the blades are not set too deeply as to penetrate below the narrow band of humus. Removal of the humus or its dilution with the underlying parent sand will greatly reduce the germination capacity of the seed. All turves must be collected and discarded off site. Following turf removal, a light rake or scarification treatment would create a series of shallow grooves within the surface to further protect and facilitate the germinating sward.

(2) *Mechanical treatments*. This will involve both cutting and scarification to (a) reduce the cutting height to ground level and (b) remove the majority of thatch from the surface.

Following flailing or cutting the grass sward to ground level, it will be necessary to employ one of the modern heavy duty flail mower/ scarifiers with collecting hopper or, alternatively, a separate trailed scarifier followed by collection unit. The operation should be continued until either the underlying humus is exposed or until conditions become too wet to continue, whereupon it will be necessary to suspend the work until the next layer of the thatch has sufficiently dried. With successive passes much of the surface fibre can be removed. Again, care should be taken not to destroy the underlying humus layer.

Because of the difficulties of effectively carrying out this work, it would be appropriate to gain experience over a suitably sized area out of immediate play, monitoring the results upon completion.

Reinstating and Managing Mature Heather Swards
A range of age classes of heather would normally be desirable so as to support a maximum range of associated wildlife. Whilst certain species favour old, degenerate heather, others favour areas of short to mature heather.

On the golf course, given the limited areas available, it may not be possible to create the diversity of age and/or the range of conditions desired. We must therefore accept from the outset that whilst some species may be favoured, others may be excluded. Management, however, will be necessary if the survival and character of the heathland site is to be retained.

In order to obtain or maintain the desired variation in age, form and structure of the heather stands, it will be necessary to consider rotational management. This will ultimately be dependent upon the size of area available and will involve splitting the heaths into several portions, carrying out the management works on a phased, possibly annual, basis. Concentrating on one or two areas each year will generate the variety of age desired and would not unduly over-burden the greenstaff. Size of the whole area will be a critical factor in determining how many portions can be ascribed and indeed in determining the most appropriate management techniques. Obviously, relatively small areas would be best maintained as single stands benefiting from a single management treatment on an infrequent but continuous and sustainable frequency.

Burning. This is unpredictable, requiring considerable planning, discretion and vigilance. It is practised on some heathland golf courses and whilst burning does, if carried out correctly, offer a good method of maintaining vegetation quality, it is, however, of very limited application, especially on the golf course for the following reasons.

Burning can kill invertebrates and reptiles and may destroy scarce plants. On all but the largest sites, possibly over 400 hectares, it can have catastrophic effects on wildlife populations. It is a very exacting technique with respect to temperature, the burn must be controlled at a maximum 400-500°C, taking care to ensure that the heat does not penetrate more than a few millimetres into the surface debris and underlying humus. Burns in excess of this may penetrate much deeper, killing the seed rather than stimulating its germination. Indeed, it is likely that the more mature, previously neglected areas of heather will, through time, build up a considerable layer of open debris at the surface and this, together with the bulk of woody above-ground shoot material, will encourage burns in excess of 1500°C. Such extremes in temperature may reach up to 15 cm depth, killing viable seed and root, so inhibiting both seed and vegetative regeneration. Similarly, much of the associated wildlife seeking protection immediately below ground will inevitably be killed. To achieve a correct burn, the heather condition must be assessed and the height, density and age of each individual stand noted. Burning may be necessary on a 10 to 12 year rotation or as the heather reaches between 20 and 30 cm in height. Special care must be taken when the heather is mixed with bracken or competing grasses. Ideally, the heather should be burnt whilst in its building phase, which is rarely possible on golf courses having previously neglected these duties.

Two or three people must be in attendance to ensure control of the flames and to extinguish the fire as soon as the desired results have been achieved. A light and rapid burn is required and is therefore dependent upon correct wind speed, force 2 to 3 being optimum.

Burning is governed by law. The statutory burning season extends between 1st November and 31st March in the lowlands and between 1st October and 15th April in the uplands and so includes the wettest periods of the year. Written notice of the intent to burn should be given to owners, occupants and neighbours not less than 24 hours or more than 7 days before commencing. Fires should not be lit between sunset and sunrise.

Burning should be restricted to 1 hectare at a time, preferably creating sinuous edges to the margin of the burn so as to increase the length of the interface between young and old stands.

Small burns annually may be preferable on the golf course as larger burns would necessitate and depend upon wildlife recolonising from surrounding land. Smaller burns will allow recolonisation from within.

Mechanical Methods
Cutting. Heather cutting can be a valuable adjunct to burning, especially in the periodic removal of above-ground biomass or, and especially on the golf course, as a sole main management tool.

Cutting has the following advantages:

It is not as weather-dependent nor as exacting and is therefore much more easily executed. There is usually much less damage to associated wildlife, though it will still be necessary to phase the works over areas of the course on an annual rotation. It is preferred on smaller sites with often much fewer problems being encountered through erosion and associated droughting.

Depending upon the position and function of the heather stand, an appropriate topping rotation may involve a single cut each year or an infrequent cut possibly every 8 or 10 years. Heather older than this will not respond well to cutting and subsequent regrowth may be poor.

Cutting should be carried out after seed set during December to late February. The initial height of cut should be between 100 and 125 mm

(4 and 5 in.) so as not to lose the lowest dormant buds. Successive cutting thereafter should follow an appropriate frequency so as to maintain the preferred height.

It may well be on those courses where heather has been neglected for a number of years that the plants have lost their capacity to regenerate and that total clearance and seed reinstatement may be necessary as outlined further below.

Machinery for Cutting the Heather Sward
Forage harvesters, swipes, the heavy duty industrial flail/scarifiers are all used and all have merit in different situations. Where the terrain is difficult with underlying boulders possibly hidden from view, blades may be better than chains. The latter do tend to break when contacting larger stones. Flail mowers may not be robust enough under such circumstances. Forage harvesters and the heavy duty modern verti-flails are most suitable for less damaging and more even terrain. Indeed, the vertiflail/scarifier will double as a fairway scarifier and, with its high tip hopper, will collect all arisings, so making it extremely useful in reinstating areas formerly overgrown with scrub or weedgrasses.

The double-chop forage harvester has been used successfully and is basically an agricultural cylinder mower 1.5 metres wide which delivers the vegetation into a trailer by means of a blower or chute. The harvester would need a tractor capable of delivering 70 hp with 4-wheel drive being essential. The forest harvester has the advantage of producing a clean cut in all ages of heather compared with the swipe or flail type machines which tend to rip the older, more woody plants. Cutting height control can be finely adjusted on the tractor hydraulics, allowing small scale undulations to be negotiated. The speed of the operation will be determined by the terrain and age of vegetation stands and may therefore vary between 1 km/h on the roughest terrain to 10 km/h on the flat, managed areas.

Regeneration of Old Degenerate Heather Swards
Heather regenerates either from the base of the cut or burnt stem, or by germination from seed. The capacity of heather to regenerate from its basal lateral buds (known as its vegetative capacity) will decline progressively with age.

During the first 15 or so years of its life cycle the vegetative capacity may be high (90% or so) from cutting. After this period, however, and once the stems have become increasingly woody (mature to degenerate phases of its life cycle), the vegetative capacity may drop to around 10%. Therefore in older stands of heather, germination of seed becomes

PLATE 8. Heather becomes increasingly woody with age.

much more important and often the only means of perpetuating heather dominance. Because seed germination is dependent upon light, cutting alone may not be sufficient to stimulate or break its dormancy. There will therefore be a need to disturb or remove the underlying mat of litter so as to expose the underlying humus layer.

Given the above, the first operation must be to cut the heather to ground level using appropriate equipment capable of collecting and discarding the woody plant material. This operation should then be followed by a series of scarification treatments using the heavy duty flail/scarifier or other tractor-drawn unit capable of collecting all arisings. The number of passes will be dependent upon the overall depth of litter encountered. Having thoroughly disturbed but not rotovated the surface, there are several options available for encouraging seed germination and establishment.

PLATE 9. Mechanical cutting and scarification to clear the surface debris – note presence of scarification lines in the surface humus.

These include: leaving the surface without any further treatment; spreading brashings, i.e. the whole cut plant material, or spreading capsules, i.e. the top 50 to 75 mm (2 to 3 in.) of the cut plant material; or sowing out a nurse grass sward. The option chosen will, to some extent, depend upon the type and position of the golf course with respect to climate.

Research undertaken at the STRI (see Appendix I) has shown that leaving the surface exposed following scarification work did encourage a significant seed establishment.

PLATE 10. Heather regrowth by seed.

The spreading of capsules and brashings both tended to inhibit seed germination, possibly due to their smothering effect given the relatively high rainfall area where the trial works were conducted (average annual rainfall [1960-1988] 935 mm).

In the lowland heaths of Southern Britain surface drying and erosion is highly likely and this, together with excessive sunlight and the prolonged drought, may without protection from capsules, brashings or the nurse grass compromise seed germination and/or seedling survival.

Research undertaken by British Gas in conjunction with the Environmental Advisory Unit of the University of Liverpool has shown that optimum weights of heather capsules may be in the order of 2250 kg/ha. Brashings could alternatively be used at a spreading rate of 1000 to 2000 kg/ha.

In a number of trials, grasses acting as a "companion" or "nurse" to the heather seedlings have been used with considerable success. These would have particular advantage in stabilising bare and/or eroding areas until the heather becomes established. The grasses used, however, must not be of an aggressive or highly competitive nature. In the STRI trials

(Appendix I) the sowing of a nurse grass did result in significantly more heather seedlings than either brashings or capsules alone. This possibly further suggests that both capsules and brashings in the uplands may, in quantity, smother and suppress heather seed germination.

Using nurse grasses may necessitate the need for early chemical treatments to ensure that the predominance of heather continues over the grass sward.

Pest Problems on Heather
Several courses have experienced a russet discoloration of the heather and complete defoliation of the leaf material. Inspection of the litter layer reveals the grubs or larvae of the heather beetle (*Lochmaea suturalis*). The overall effect of the larvae grazing the heather can be quite serious, particularly in older, mature plants where the vegetative capacity has been significantly reduced.

Young plants do appear to be less affected, possibly due to their increased vigour and overall healthier condition.

The main problem facing clubs is how to control or stop further damage from occurring. To answer this, one must understand some of the basic factors of the beetle's life cycle.

PLATE 11. Heavily predated stand of mature heather.

40

PLATE 12. Larval stage *Lochmaea suturalis.*

Lochmaea suturalis undergoes three stages of development (egg, larvae and adult). The adult emerges from within the litter layer during April/ May having overwintered in the larval stage. The adult will lay its eggs in the sphagnum moss residing at the base of the heather plants. Larvae emerge during June/July feeding on the heather shoots until mid August whereupon they retreat back to the soil for the winter period.

Control
Spraying using pesticides is rarely successful. The larvae at the first sign of disturbance fall from the plants to the ground and are therefore offered protection by the canopy. Similarly, by the time the devastation to the foliage has been fully appreciated, it is likely that the larvae have gone to ground for the winter. The main natural predator of *Lochmaea suturalis* is the ladybird and it is likely that these would be killed by the chemical. During the main flowering season many insects, including bumble bees, will be feeding and would undoubtedly be severely affected.

The greenkeeper must therefore implement a programme of physical cutting and scarification to (a) reduce the woody material and improve structural quality of the heather, and (b) remove the larvae via scarification techniques aimed at disturbing the trash layer.

Regeneration thereafter may, in the main, be dependent upon seed, possibly with some vegetative growth from the cut plants.

Bracken Control

Bracken (*Pteridium aquilinum*) is often thought of as a total undesirable on the golf course. This, in the majority of cases, may be true but there are instances where bracken can have ecological benefit.

Ecology

Bracken is an opportunist able to associate with quite diverse communities. It usually achieves dominance both in the open and in gaps and clearings within open woodlands. It may be suppressed as the tree canopy develops. Once dominant, its large leaves or fronds cast a dense shade which, together with the large quantity of litter, tend to totally suppress the growth of higher plant species, including heather and the finer grasses of the heathland.

Occasionally bracken-dominated stands may be ecologically quite important, forming communities which are relatively species rich. In such instances bracken can effectively suppress aggressive summer flowering species of both grass and flowers, and because the fronds are late in unfolding, vernal or spring flowering communities may be preserved. In the cleared copse areas or open wood/screen margins, bluebell, wood sorrel and possibly even rarer species may be found.

Bracken-dominated stands do offer cover for the nests of several birds, though actual numbers recorded in bracken are much less than would be found in most other habitat types. On the heathland golf course the change in habitat type from predominantly relatively open heath grassland to bracken may result in a total loss of reptiles and snakes as the open basking areas are reduced.

The very invasive nature of bracken in Britain is normally thought to cause an alarming reduction in habitat quality, often resulting in the further fragmentation of already small, fragmented roughs.

Management

Physical cutting and chemical spraying are the two most successful methods of bracken control. Both are expensive in resource and/or labour and have various problems associated with them, not least the need for continued or periodic retreatment to prevent regrowth. Because bracken can increase the nutrient status of its surroundings, there is often a tendency towards its replacement with fast growing, weedy species rather than the slower growing, desirable flora.

Before any management work is undertaken, an ecological appraisal would be useful to fully evaluate the ecological potential of the communities present.

A three-year programme of eradication involving both physical and chemical control may be most successful, with physical control methods being adopted in the first and third years.

The careful use of selected herbicides has proven to be very effective in bracken control. Spray drift can, however, kill underlying heather. Spraying should be carried out during calm, still periods in June once the fronds have fully opened in strict accordance with the manufacturer's recommendations.

Physical control should concentrate upon cutting or physically lifting and should be carried out when the first fronds have fully opened during late June/July and when the nutrient reserves in the rhizomes are low. Increasing the number of cuts will accelerate the eradication process and bring about a more rapid control.

Indeed, trial work undertaken within the brecklands of South West Norfolk using repeated cutting techniques has proved particularly successful. A swipe or flail used on three occasions at six week intervals throughout the growing period, i.e. June to September, to exhaust the underground rhizomes repeated over two years can severely weaken the bracken. A suitable height of cut would be 10 cm (4 in.) and the litter arising can be left or collected depending upon position with respect to play.

Ideal equipment would include the heavy duty flail/scarifiers, the forage harvesters or a suitable flail or swipe.

The Management of Gorse
Ecology
Gorse (*Ulex europaeus*) is a native component of the British heathlands and one which is often quick to colonise favourable areas where clearance of scrub or woodland has been effected and grazing ceased. Gorse can be a particularly important member of the heathland community, often supporting a higher invertebrate and vertebrate density than the neighbouring heather. It provides nest sites, shelter and song posts for a host of birds, including the stonechat, whinchat and, in areas of Dorset and Hampshire, the Dartford warbler. Much of this interest is heavily dependent upon the state and condition of the gorse, i.e. whether it is bushy with a close canopy and continuous with other associated vegetation types or whether it is isolated, unkempt and leggy with a spreading open canopy. Gorse, like heather, does have a final life cycle of around 30 years, during which time the shrub will pass through an initial pioneer or seedling establishment phase into the building or juvenile stage lasting for up to 15 years. Active management at this

time will help to maintain the quality of growth, i.e. the closed, dense and bushy canopy structure. If left, the shrub will pass through and into the mature and finally degenerate stages where the intrinsic capacity for vegetative regrowth may be severely reduced. Indeed, almost all of the wildlife interest is generally associated with the young and mature phases. During the degenerate stages, when the plants become open, gappy and heavily wooded, the capacity for vegetative regrowth or recovery after cutting may be reduced to approximately one tenth of that observed during the building phase.

If gorse is to remain an integral feature of the golf course, then active but carefully timed management will be essential.

Problems Encountered
Possibly, the main problems found with respect to the maintenance of gorse on the golf course are related to both inappropriate management or total neglect. Indeed, it may only be when gorse becomes visually unsightly through its rank, woody growth form and open canopy that the club will realise and possibly accept the need for active management. Other clubs, through a lack of understanding as to the growth characteristics of gorse, may practice frequent but inappropriate cutting so as to create a topiary effect of lollipop-shaped individuals quite artificial and out of keeping with the rest of the course.

PLATE 13. Gorse: mature to degenerate stage.

44

Management
The aim should be to maintain a good structural diversity of age and form through rotational management. Both young and mature phases are desirable, being managed so as to retain their overall dense structure. Depending upon the quality of vegetation present, a rotation may involve cutting on a 3 to 15 year basis.

Where gorse is found to be problematic, i.e. in species-rich grasslands such as are present through the southern downlands, scrub clearance may be required, involving hand or machine techniques so as to halt or slow down the natural succession that would otherwise occur.

Clearance or cutting of gorse can leave unsightly areas almost entirely devoid of vegetation. The remaining cut stumps can, in many instances, be quite dangerous to the golfer seeking stray golf balls. When clearing part of any mature to degenerate stand, the remaining backdrop of woody stem material may be unacceptable with respect to its position on the course.

Cutting is usually the main method employed on the golf course, though burning, employed in larger semi-natural heathland situations, may have limited use on one or two larger courses. The aim of the management work should be to maintain dense, bushy shrubs in their juvenile to mature stage, i.e. between 5 and 15 years, cutting on an accepted rotation so as to maintain these desired growth characteristics.

Where the shrubs have progressed into the late mature to degenerate stage, the capacity for vegetative regrowth may decline markedly necessitating the removal of all woody and leggy material, cutting back to ground level or to the first lateral bud. Leaving lengthy stems may, given some vegetative regrowth, result in the production of artificial lollipops of low ecological significance.

Due to the lack of potential regrowth at this stage, more attention may need to be given to encouraging the underlying seed present but dormant within the seed bank. The seed will require light to germinate and this will therefore involve a degree of surface preparation so as to remove the accumulation of leaf and shoot material, so uncovering and exposing the underlying humus layer and dormant seed bank. This may involve scarification using a heavy duty vertiflail/scarifier or a hand rake depending upon area and nature of surface. The cut material and surface debris should be lifted and discarded from site, possibly to be respread over prepared areas of the course (see below). Failure to lift, burn or discard the surface debris will inhibit and suppress germination, possibly favouring bracken invasion. If rabbits are common, suitable protection

PLATE 14. Vegetative regrowth from cut stems.

may be required. Reinstatement by seed can be quite effective and, indeed, rapid providing that frequent irrigation is maintained through the early establishment phase.

Introducing Gorse to New Areas of the Course
If gorse is absent or scarce but desired, it can be established providing that suitable ground conditions have been prepared. The optimum pH is around 4.5 and this may be produced via appropriate applications of elemental sulphur or aluminium sulphate. Laboratory testing would be necessary to determine appropriate rates. Establishment may be further aided by the presence of burnt ash from either heather or gorse so as to increase the potash component within the soil.

Gorse can be purchased as seed, root-trained or container-grown stock, all of which have some merit at particular sites. Following planting, the gorse must be protected from predation using appropriate shrub guards and from drying out by frequent watering until established.

If gorse is plentiful within the local countryside, a suitable donor site may be locally available from which seed can be collected. This would involve physical scraping or the hire of an industrial-type vacuum which could then be used to collect the seed from underneath existing plants. Once collected, the seed would be spread over prepared surfaces at a rate of approximately 400 to 500 g/m^2 of fresh material. This rate assumes a degree of surface debris present within the mix. Ideally, seed should be applied during early spring, i.e. February to March, or alternatively during the autumn period between September and November when climatic conditions are most favourable.

Surface preparation may involve one or more chemical weed treatments so as to kill the existing surface vegetation, leaving these areas one month or so before removing the dead grass and weeds through successive heavy duty scarification work. Alternatively, if the area chosen is in immediate play, heavy and intensive scarification work alone may be sufficient to create gaps within the surface into which the seed or seedlings can be planted. Any amelioration of the soil pH should be completed well in advance of planting.

Ideally the root-trained or container-grown plants should be notch- or pit-planted during the autumn/winter period at close spacings not exceeding 1 m^2 (0.5 to 0.75 m^2 being ideal). Once planted, the surface around each plant should be firmed, and watering and protection thereafter continued throughout the establishment period.

Contracting Out Heathland Management
The management of several of the larger remaining fragments of heathland is carried out by contract labour. What are the possibilities available to golf and what would be the advantages/disadvantages of this approach?

This approach will avoid the need for some equipment, although many golf clubs have or are considering purchasing suitable heavy duty flail mowers/scarifiers for other routine maintenance work.

A reputable contractor would need to be prepared to treat relatively small fragments on a phased, annual basis, and fees and travel costs therefore would be an important consideration.

Reputable contractors are available and can usually be found by asking a few specific questions related to the management strategies. Obviously, a contractor with enthusiasm for heathland conservation would be a good candidate.

Away from golf, several sites, particularly in Hampshire, The Weald and Thames Valley, have been considerably improved using contract labour and resources.

Although reputable contractors are competent as to which trees should be retained or removed, a close liaison and vigil from the Head Greenkeeper would be important so as not to remove those of strategic importance to the course.

On the heathland course a good contractor or even paid "ecological management officer" responsible on a full-time basis to the Head Greenkeeper would be a very positive way forward, ensuring continuity and sustainability of the heathland resource and its management.

2.2 WOODLANDS:
THEIR DEVELOPMENT AND MANAGEMENT

Rationale for Management

Woodlands represent one of our most important habitats for wildlife. On the golf course, trees either singly or in groups, i.e. as copses, screens or woodlands, provide fairway separation, hole individuality and contribute significantly to the strategic and playing quality of a given hole. Trees, by their presence, offer relaxed, pleasant surroundings of varied seasonal interest and, if integral with the surrounding landscape, will offer a reassuring sense of naturalness.

PLATE 15. Trees offer a relaxed and pleasant surrounding for golf.

Because of the secondary nature of the woodlands, i.e. being planted by man through the 19th and 20th Centuries, they are prone to natural succession, including weed invasion and gradual deterioration through the lack of self-renewal processes. Management is therefore required if their structural integrity and diversity is to be maintained.

Problems Encountered

Of the numerous copses and woodlands assessed, the STRI has found the main problems to be:

[a]   even aged stands of one species, of which pine, birch and wild cherry are commonly encountered;

PLATE 16. Inappropriate planting using one species in localised groupings, reducing visual and ecological interest.

[b]   little or no natural regeneration with consequent poor structural age or species diversity;

[c]   even density, often very wide spacings between all trees, necessitating constant and frequent attention in the form of over-tidying from greenkeeping staff;

[d]   habitat deterioration through management neglect, often resulting in overgrowth and massive invasion of weed species such as rhododendron, bramble or sycamore;

[e]   inappropriate species reducing ecological/conservation signif-icance of habitat and possibly reduction in overall aesthetic and strategic character, Leylandii and lombardy poplar being most frequently encountered.

Management Objectives

[a]   To increase:

(i)   structural diversity, from high canopy, canopy trees to the lower growing shrubs of the understorey and wood edge;

(ii) species and age diversity by utilising an appropriate native assemblage of species offering differing relative growth rates to ensure long term continuity.

[b]   To create "semi-natural" features by strengthening existing plantings and reducing routine intensive maintenance, particularly in the woodland/copse centres.

50

[c]   To create a variation in density of spacing (between 1.5 and 2 metres and up to 5 metres). Open areas or clearings in more substantial woodlands will be of major ecological importance and should, where possible, be included.

[d]   To link otherwise isolated features so as to extend the natural bridging through the course.

Management Limitations
The ecological management programme must consider speed of play and facilitation of ball from at least the woodland margins.

Golf clubs do tend to favour tree planting at the expense of other equally important ecological management programmes, i.e. restoration of grasslands, hedgerows, water features, etc., and it is therefore important to give equal consideration to these. Over-planting or the indiscriminate use of trees should be avoided.

Views and vistas both through the course and out into the surrounding countryside should be retained as they do form an important and significant feature of the course.

Management Prescription
New Planting
The first operation when considering any new planting, either a full new development or an extension of an existing feature, will be to determine the former character, i.e. habitat type. Here, an ecological appraisal would help in determining suitable locations. The locations should be appropriately marked.

The woodland/copse margin should follow informal, natural contours in accordance with the topography of the site and acute zigzags should be avoided. Do not plant any tree closer than 8 metres to putting surfaces.

Having determined locations and areas, a suitable planting strategy together with species mixture will be required. Identify the local tree types, paying particular attention to those within the local landscape, i.e. off the course. These trees will be better adapted to local climatic and physical constraints.

Table 1 gives a typical percentage species composition for a moderate to heavy loam site with moderate exposure. Note that ash and oak are dominant, with birch, alder and Scots pine forming the main nurse trees.

Species	Mixed Wood/Copse % Composition	Shrub/Wood Edge % Composition	Hedgerow % Composition
Trees			
Alnus glutinosa (Alder)	7	5	As standards
Betula pubescens (Birch)	5		
Betula pendula (Birch)	13	5	
Fraxinus excelsior (Ash)	18		As standards
Pinus sylvestris (Scots pine)	18		
Populus tremula (Aspen)	5		
Quercus robur (Oak)	24	10	As standards
Sorbus aucuparia (Rowan)	5	10	
Sorbus aria (Whitebeam)	5	5	
	100%		
Shrubs			
Corylus avellana (Hazel)	20	20	15
Crataegus monogyna (Hawthorn)	20	18	40
Prunus spinosa (Blackthorn)	18		40
Salix caprea (Goat willow)	12	4	
Salix cinerea (Sallow)	12	5	
Ligustrum vulgare (Privet)	2	4	5
Ilex aquifolium (Holly)	8	8	
Acer campestre (Field maple)	8	6	
	100%	100%	100%

TABLE 1. Mixed woodland % Planting Association.

All trees selected should, where possible, be native in origin and in keeping with local conditions. Care must be taken not to use inappropriate trees, i.e. with undesirable growth characteristics. Poplar are notorious for their water-seeking ability, roots have been located in drainage pipes over distances of 40 metres.

Certain trees, such as sycamore, sweet chestnut and horse chestnut, possess large, soft leaves which can cause problems on putting areas and should generally be excluded. Sycamore is useful in very exposed situations, e.g. coastal regions. Horse chestnut may encourage trespass and vandalism in search for conkers.

Standards or forestry transplants. The next stage will be to determine whether to select standards or the smaller whips or forestry transplants. All have application in certain situations but standards are generally quite expensive and may suffer substantially from damage through stray golf balls, particularly in the early years of establishment. Standards do tend to grow slowly, taking considerably longer to achieve a reasonable canopy height.

Forestry transplants, normally 1 + 0 or 1 + 1 (number of years in nursery plus number of years outside), between 30 and 90 cm in height are very cheap to purchase and do grow rapidly in the early years (particularly if planted at close spacings so as to increase competition for the available light resource).

Standards would normally be planted at 4 metre spacings, whereas forestry transplants may assume spacings between 1.5 and 3 metres.

PLATE 17. Standard trees planted at wide spacings are costly to purchase and plant, and are susceptible to golf ball damage.

Standards should be pit-planted in pits of sufficient size so as to accommodate the bare roots. The pit size will be dependent upon size of standards purchased. Before planting, it may be necessary to add in the order of 100 g of a balanced NPK fertilizer, i.e. 10:15:10, to each pit. The tree should be planted centrally in the excavated pit with a stake not exceeding one third of the height of the tree positioned 100 mm from the tree on the windward side. Backfill with subsoil then topsoil, firming the soil in layers to a height not exceeding the root collar.

Irrigation may be required during the early establishment period.

Forestry trees can be notch-planted. This is a technique whereby an 'H' or 'L'-shaped notch is dug and lifted and the trees inserted and firmed to the height of the root collar. No fertilizer would normally be required though this will obviously be dependent upon the results of a soil chemical analysis to determine the chemical nature of the soil.

The smaller trees should be planted in a random or staggered arrangement in irregular single species groupings and in multiples of four, i.e. 4, 8, 16 to 32, in and amongst the individual nurse trees. Groups of shrubs planted in and amongst the chosen tree species will further help protect and nurse the main trees through their early establishment.

PLATE 18. A three-year old plantation. Forestry transplants are cheap to purchase and may rapidly out-grow standards to form a more natural woodland. Thinning will be an integral component of their management.

In many instances, both forestry transplants and standards are used together. The standards do offer an immediate effect, with the forestry trees surviving and possibly out-growing the standards in time to form the established woodland feature. Protection using appropriate tree guards will be important in encouraging early tree growth and should not be overlooked. Tree guards also protect the trees from grazing animals and spray drift during the period of aftercare following planting. When planting, it will be necessary to consider the woodland margin as being distinct from the wood centre or wood edge.

The woodland margin may be described as a band width of 4-6 metres around the edge of the woodland, although size of this area may vary depending on the size of the copse or woodland and its position relative to play. This would normally be cut on a regular basis, possibly at a similar frequency to that prescribed for the semi-rough. Once established, the woodland centre, excluding the woodland margin, should be left uncut. During the first few years of establishment, however, and until a reasonable canopy has established some infrequent cutting together with appropriate weed control around each individual tree will be required.

Aftercare. Young trees planted into a productive grass sward do often show classic stress symptoms, i.e. sparse small leaves, shoot die back and a yellowing or browning of leaves caused by nitrogen deficiency, water stress or increased competition. Tree survival and growth can be significantly reduced due to the presence of coarse and productive grass species and mowing is ineffective in reducing this. Indeed, mowing will tend to increase the vigour of a grass sward, further increasing soil moisture deficit and decreasing tree vigour.

There are several methods of controlling weeds around newly planted trees but all involve their complete removal. The careful use of herbicides is effective and will involve spraying around each tree base to a nominal 300 mm radius (600 mm diameter). The weed-free zone should be maintained for at least three years into the early establishment period. Mulch mats made of black polythene, for example, have been found to be quite effective, helping to smother or prevent the further establishment of weed species. Tree tubes will offer some protection from the competing grass sward but their main advantage will be in protection from mammal and rodent damage whilst providing a favourable microclimate around individual trees, so acting like a mini-greenhouse.

Beating-up. Some losses after planting are almost inevitable and it will be necessary to replace dead, deformed or dying trees usually one year after planting. Many dead trees, particularly standards, possibly due to their initial cost of purchase and resource spent planting, are retained when obviously dead and are often still given appropriate aftercare treatments in the hope of reviving them. These trees should be removed and replaced with more healthy stock.

Thinning. Thinning will form an integral part of any management/development programme and must not be overlooked. Thinning may involve possibly two separate treatments at appropriate intervals depending upon speed of growth of the trees, with the aim being to maintain good quality trees at the final desired spacings dependent upon position and function. It will be necessary to monitor the progress of the plantings on an annual basis with appropriate wording being written into the management programme/course policy document, to remove any dead, dying, damaged or deformed trees, replacing these as necessary.

Other Considerations
Woodland Edge
The semi-natural woodlands/copses will benefit from a woodland edge of suitable shrubs planted in a broken fashion around the main planting. The wood edge differs from the main planting in respect of its position and function and in view of the species used and the spacings adopted. Given the close proximity, i.e. 1.5 metre spacings of the planting, care will be required when considering appropriate location. The wood edge is ecologically important and will improve the overall woodland/copse condition and visual perspective.

PLATE 19. The wood edge in time will screen the woodland centre and may encourage understorey regeneration.

The edge, planted sensibly in relation to play and habitat conditions, will take away the abrupt visual appearance of the main planting by creating a more natural domed effect and will tidy an otherwise unkempt ground layer, possibly under criticism of members. The edge will help to retain leaf litter and will encourage natural regeneration within the centre, so accelerating and perpetuating the natural woodland cycle.

Single species groupings of understorey shrubs should be selected, planted at 1.5 metre spacings in a random or staggered arrangement.

56

The edge should be varied and broken in appearance (never assuming regimental straight lines) and should follow the natural contouring and informality of the fairways.

Making Use of Deadwood
Deadwood includes twigs to whole roots and leaf litter to whole trunks. It is often a problem to greenkeepers and golfers and is normally cleared off site to improve the aesthetic, visual and playing quality of the course.

Deadwood is an essential and fundamental component of woodland ecosystems with well over half of the timber in any natural woodlands supporting some stage of decomposition. On the golf course, there may be a clear conflict or dilemma between the need to conserve deadwood and maintain an overall tidy appearance.

Out of immediate play, dead or dying trees should be retained. Obviously an assessment will be necessary to determine just how safe they are in relation to their position. If removal is inevitable, consider the selective removal of the dead boughs, rather than the whole tree. Deadwood within woodland areas should be left *in situ*. Collected wood, where possible, should be cut into the largest manageable lengths and stockpiled or scattered within the centre of the more substantial woodland areas. Brushwood heaps also offer excellent habitats for many creatures, although they should not be left on the lowland heathland course due to the risk of fire.

Hollow trees are often felled unnecessarily on the golf course in the belief that they are either dead or dying. Recent research work has shown that fungi, once thought heavily parasitic and responsible for their decay, are actually beneficial. By hollowing out the centre of the tree, fungi help to reduce its weight and solidity, allowing much greater flexibility and therefore increasing resistance to wind and storm damage. Indeed, it is suspected that if many of the southern beeches destroyed in the storms of 1989/90 were hollow, then the total losses would have been considerably reduced.

Tree Planting in Exposed Situations
There are several factors likely to influence the susceptibility of trees under exposed conditions. These include **windiness**. Wind speed varies widely across the country and whilst North and West Britain together with the coastal areas experience regular strong winds, other parts of the country may receive considerably reduced wind velocities. **Elevation** will influence wind speed and frequency, rainfall in elevated areas may also increase leading to wetter soil conditions and a reduction in root growth and soil shear strength. Wind exposure will be modified

by the site's **topography**, the influence of surrounding land in creating turbulence, shelter, funnelling or wind acceleration must be taken into account. Uprooting will occur when the lateral forces applied to a tree overcome the root anchorage and so **soil conditions and rooting depth** will also be of major importance in determining tolerance to exposure. The degree to which a tree root system can resist overturning is largely related to root growth and structure and to the depth and amount of soil contained within and around the root plate. Trees growing on heavier, wet or highly organic soils are likely to be uprooted more easily than those on better drained sites due to the shallower rooting and increased incidence of root rot. Similarly, trees growing on rocky, stony soils will also tend to be less wind-firm than those growing on stone-free soils. Although there are very few data available to determine the relative stabilities of different woodland trees, it does appear that certain species are much more stable under certain circumstances than others. Ash appears to be very stable, as does Norway maple, horse chestnut, London plane, English oak and sycamore. Lime, beech, Turkey oak and poplar are very unstable. It is therefore important to select carefully in exposed situations. Because a tree's shape and size will exacerbate the forces exerted upon it, it may be worth considering planting trees which will remain relatively small. Indeed, on the links and exposed heathland courses very few large trees are to be found. Suitable species having a maximum height of less than 15 metres would include aspen, bird cherry, common osier, crab apple, field maple, gean, goat willow, hawthorn, hazel, holly, rowan, whitebeam, white poplar and yew.

Trees planted relatively closely protected b neighbouring or adjacent trees will tend to be more wind-stable than thin stands.

Coppicing may be desirable in some situations, particularly in the larger and more central woodland areas, and will involve the cutting back of stems on a regular basis depending upon tree species. All broad-leaved species, with the exception of beech in drier eastern counties, can be managed as coppice. Rotation lengths may vary between 8 and 20 years. Coppice would indeed be a useful management option on those sites with a reduced topsoil depth and poor soil structure.

To improve tree stability is to prevent shallow rooting. This will involve the provision of sufficient (1 m^3), well drained, non-compact and reasonably fine textured soil. Restrictive soil layers will, like in fine turf situations, prevent and restrict root penetration, impair drainage and so further reduce anchoring and soil shear strength.

Hedgerows
Hedgerows have been part of our landscape heritage for over a thousand

years. Indeed, the first live hawthorn hedge can be traced back to the time of the Norman Conquest. Today, with the intensification of arable farming and the need to create fields of sufficient size, the widescale destruction and grubbing out of the hedgerows has been dramatic. Indeed, it has been estimated that between 1946 and 1974 over 140,000 miles of hedgerow were lost. Possibly 20,000 miles of the total would include non-agricultural losses. Many of the remaining hedges are possibly only 100 or 200 years old, but there are remnants whose history can be traced back to well over 800 years and more.

Interestingly, many of these important historic features can be found and are indeed being retained at least in some form on the golf course. Hedgerows are essentially man-made and their overall character and form is largely dependent upon management. Many of these traditional features represented on golf courses are tending to lose their structural integrity largely through management neglect. Without management, the hedge will gradually become top-heavy, displaying coarse, unkempt growth, leading to gaps within the base and at intervals along its length. Well maintained hedges form a complete ecosystem and an extension of the woodland environment and are therefore important for a large number of bird, insect and other animal and plant species.

The overall state or condition of the hedge will influence which wildlife is favoured and which is excluded. Blackbirds and song thrushes, for example, favour tall, bushy hedges, whilst tits prefer taller standard trees to be present. Wrens and robins are attracted by dense hedges offering a diversity of shrub species. The degree of cover available around the base of the hedge, including that in ditches, is also important for many species.

Given the above, it is clear that there is no ideal hedge but some guidelines, however, can be formulated:

[a] The average hedge height should be around 1.4 metres with an average width of 1.2 metres.
[b] Management should be geared towards removing the previous year's growth only, so as to retain the density of form and structure throughout.
[c] The associated ditching, if present, should not be intensively managed.

Management
If allowed to grow unchecked, hedges will gradually develop into thin, open, mature shrubs occupying an ever-increasing area of ground. They will become thinner at the base due to the shading effect of the vegetation

above, so ceasing to achieve the function of screening and stockproofing, this being particularly important around the perimeter to reduce vandalism and trespass on the course. Screening will also be particularly important around the perimeter, especially where hedges demarcate the barrier between the golf course and associated roads or housing.

In order to preserve them as tough and impenetrable barriers, a scheme of regular care will be needed.

The most usual method of hedge maintenance is periodic trimming which, besides producing a neat and orderly appearance, will stimulate growth of side shoots, so increasing the bushiness of the hedge and its stockproof qualities. This can be undertaken using a flail or similar tractor-mounted implement. The shape or profile of the hedge is of importance, particularly with respect to the number of runs required to cut it. Possibly, the easiest shape to achieve is an 'A' shape which requires only two runs, one each side. Its slope facilitates the passage of air, so providing an effective windbreak. Extensive cutting at the top will encourage active growth lower down, so providing a firm, trespass-proof barrier. Providing the hedge is cut to around 1.8-2.0 metres, the lower areas will provide good cover and habitat for wildlife. A more bulky hedge can be maintained by chamfering or rounding the top corners but this will involve possibly four runs.

In the interests of safety, it will be necessary to inspect the length of the hedge prior to cutting, removing any obstacles that could either damage the machinery or injure passing golfers.

An important aspect of hedge trimming often overlooked is the need to preserve desirable saplings, such as oak for example, which should be encouraged to grow into and form large, mature standard trees. Standard trees planted within the hedge line or the natural regeneration being encouraged to form more substantial features should be identified (possibly tagged) before cutting, and extreme care is advised when cutting around these.

Filling in the Gaps
As outlined above, many hedges are losing their structural integrity, such that it will be necessary to underplant and reinstate a more dense structure. Possibly, the 45-60 cm 1 + 1 forestry transplants protected with tree tubes or guards, as appropriate, would be the most suitable and these should be planted in a double staggered row and at spacings along each row of between 300 and 450 mm (12 and 18 in.) and 300 to 450 mm between rows. The trees planted in a staggered arrangement should utilise groups of single species rather than alternating between

60

different tree/shrub types. Within the vicinity of the existing hedge it may be necessary to first trim and cut the hedge before planting directly below the canopy.

At intervals through the hedge it may be worth considering planting standard trees, possibly oak, ash or as is appropriate in respect to the surrounding vegetation types. These should be pit-planted and at variable spacings of between 8 and 20 mm apart.

Often on the golf course a formal hedge may run into a corner, leaving a fairly inaccessible area to cut. These areas could be extended using hedgerow species of similar single species groupings so as to create a more dense and natural thicket analogous to the concept of the wood edge described earlier.

Woodland Grant Aid
Grant aid for tree planting may be sought from the Borough Council or Local Authority or from the Management Initiatives of the Countryside Commission or the Woodland Grant Scheme of the Forestry Authority. The latter do provide grant aid both for woodland management and new developments. All woodlands, except those considered too small or narrow, are eligible. The thresholds have been reduced to a minimum band width of 15 metres and/or $1/4$ hectare in size. Many areas therefore on or around the golf course may fit into the scheme.

2.3 THE LINKS COURSE

PLATE 20. The links environment – utilising the natural featuring of the site.

Rationale for Management

The links golf courses situated around the coast of Great Britain do, in the popular press, receive much of the prestige for their wildlife habitat or species conservation. Very few resources are devoted to their through the green management and this may in part be due to the limited research completed to back-up any recommendations. More importantly, it is likely to be a reflection of site conditions, physical and climatic, which govern just how much or indeed how little resource needs to be given.

Dair & Schofield (1990) showed that of the coastland golf courses 919 hectares of land was given Site of Special Scientific Interest (SSSI) status. This is certainly worthy of special consideration but it must be considered in conjunction with the total SSSI land on golf courses which involves over 3076 hectares and includes all major habitat types.

Numerous examples were given in the Nature Conservancy Council's "On Course Conservation" (Schofield & Dair 1989) of representative links courses, i.e. those with SSSI status, and I would recommend this source for further reading.

PLATE 21. The natural grasslands of the links.

Problems Encountered

The main problems within the links environment on the golf course tend to be related to natural succession, i.e. the tendency for the site to become increasingly productive, leading to an increase in soil nutrient status and weed, scrub and tree invasion. Incorrect use of chemicals can influence this, as can management neglect.

A major problem frequently encountered on the links course is the inappropriate planting of conifers, namely Norway spruce planted in single species groupings, i.e. forestry blocks of one species to help screen the course for purposes of play and indeed exposure. Indiscriminate or inappropriate tree planting can severely reduce habitat quality whilst reducing the aesthetic and visual character of the course. Similarly, natural invasion of gorse, broom, sea buckthorn or white poplar if left unchecked will reduce the ecological significance of those areas of high conservation priority.

Erosion of the unstable sand dunes and sand slacks can seriously alter course character and result in the loss of important habitat types. Erosion may be caused through the natural processes of wind blow or damage through burrowing, for example, or may be man-induced by the funnelling of traffic or the indiscriminate use of golf trolleys. Random public access may also be problematic in this respect as golfers, dog-walkers and holiday-makers create instability on the seaward side of the dunes, and once sand is exposed the wind will do the rest. Where practicable, paths need to be managed to prevent such breeches. Erosion will continue until sufficient vegetation has developed and stabilised the affected area or until greenkeeping intervention has been implemented to reinstate the area and reform a fescue-dominated grass sward.

Management Objectives

Many of the seaside links courses are in a state of relative transition. The slow build up of organic material within the sands, together with the relative distance of the golf course away from the sea, tends to encourage a change from the original links land to scrub and, eventually, woodland. The semi-rough/rough and carry areas can become overrun by natural regeneration, including suckers of, for example, white poplar (*Populus alba*). This species in laying down leaf litter will eventually encourage the development of a mono-species woodland to the eventual loss of important wildlife habitat. It is therefore essential that the objectives of management are geared towards checking and reducing this.

Impenetrable thickets of poplar, sea buckthorn and, in some instances, gorse will need to be controlled and retained within discrete areas if the overall balance of habitats is not to be compromised or the overall scientific interest of the course jeopardised. It will be necessary to realise the importance of at least some management in the rough grassland areas so as to reduce organic build up and the likely decline in species diversity. Indeed, rabbit grazing has been a very important factor in maintaining the links habitat and the rich botanical diversity that may exist. On those courses where rabbits are being positively excluded, much more attention will need to be given to mechanical methods of management, i.e. cutting and litter collection, which, if undertaken sensibly in accordance with the ecological management appraisal, will not significantly alter the botanical diversity or scientific interest of the site.

Tree planting should be controlled and the use of exposure and salt-tolerant native tree types favoured before other inappropriate forestry trees.

Management Prescription

Tree and Scrub Control

It will, in the first instance, be necessary to identify which areas around the course are to be retained and which are to be managed through either thinning or tree/scrub removal.

Removal may be total or may involve the judicious and selective removal of certain problem individuals or groups. It may be necessary to thin selectively those copses being retained.

In some instances, particularly where copses are visible and in immediate play, it may be appropriate to thin and remove the centre trees, leaving a band of sufficient width around the margin. Following their removal and clearance, the centre could be then replanted with appropriate native trees and shrubs in accordance with the physical and climatic constraints of the site. The edge trees retained will act as important nurse trees, helping to reduce wind throw. Once a reasonable establishment has been achieved within the centre, the trees around the periphery of the plantations could be further thinned, removed and/or restocked, the eventual aim being to replace the alien forestry trees with more appropriate native species.

When thinning in exposed situations, it will be important to leave groups of trees rather than single individuals as these in sandier soils will tend to succumb to wind throw. Scrub invasion from gorse, broom, sea buckthorn and possibly the suckering of creeping willow (*Salix hederacea*) and white poplar will need to be controlled. Larger groups of encroaching scrub can be cleared using a heavy duty swipe or flail to cut the woody material which must then be removed from the site. The litter remaining at the surface, together with the woody stems, must then be cleared, possibly using a drott, blade grader or possibly one of the heavy industrial vertiflail/scarifiers. Thereafter, the areas cleared should be monitored and the initial blooms of scrub seedlings physically eradicated by surface disturbance. Re-invasion of bramble or other more persistent weeds could be cleared using a selective herbicide, applied using a paintbrush or weed wipe.

If left uncleared, the surface trash layer can encourage nutrient build up and the proliferation of productive broad-leaved weeds, including bracken and possibly bramble. These can be controlled by continual cutting, together with the infrequent use of herbicides.

Sea buckthorn, if planted in close proximity to greens, can produce suckers affecting surface levels and smoothness. It would here be necessary to create a solid barrier (zinc or perspex sheeting) between the green and the offending vegetation. The barrier should be positioned on the green side of the trench excavated so as to encourage balling of the roots as they come into contact with the sheet.

Constant suckering from white poplar and creeping willow can tend to be a problem, particularly in the semi-roughs, as the underground rhizomes traverse ever closer towards the fairway areas. Regular, light verticutting carried out on an annual basis will help to fine down and eradicate the invading stems without causing any undue damage to the grass sward. Once again, the heavy duty vertiflail/scarifier with high-tip hopper would be suitable for this operation. The machine may best be used with mowing blades only fitted and set to a cutting height of 25 mm (1 in.). A single pass could be carried out when all flowering plants are dormant and at a time of the year when the majority of species present will not be harmed. Possibly the most appropriate period would be mid September/late February providing ground and climatic conditions are suitable. This operation, if carried out correctly, will not only help control the woody regrowth but will also suppress the coarser, more productive (weedy) grass growth, so encouraging the development of a botanically-rich and diverse sward.

Erosion of Sand Dunes and Slacks
Erosion, if left unchecked, can lead to a progressive degradation of the dunes and may present problems to golfers as the sand continually blows out from the exposed areas. The main areas for concern tend to arise where a breach in the vegetation cover (possibly on a ridge) occurs, enlarging in accordance with the gradual loss of the underlying sand.

Because the dune passages are potentially very unstable, pathways are readily created. The greenkeeper must therefore be aware of vulnerable areas, giving particular emphasis to the most appropriate routing of traffic. Regular repairs should be undertaken involving filling in with sandy soil and returfing/reseeding. Because of the inherent problems of sand erosion, etc., turfing in many instances may be most favourable. It is important that any turf used is tolerant to the local conditions. Indeed, the majority of courses would select turves from around suitable areas of the course. Seeding can only be effective if carried out during periods of anticipated rainfall, during late summer/ early autumn and only on areas where traffic can be excluded. Even so, full establishment may, with management, take up to two years.

Sea buckthorn, although particularly invasive and problematic near the putting surfaces, can be extremely useful in helping to stabilise dunes and other areas away from immediate play.

In those areas where traffic is tending to funnel or become concentrated, it may be necessary to consider more formalised artificial pathways, possibly in the form of boardwalks constructed from slats of treated fir or pine or untreated larch, fence wire and alkathene water piping. Flying boardwalks can be useful, particularly through the wetter slacks or other areas of increased sensitivity and are less likely to become covered with sand than those resting on the surface. Although gravel and stone chippings are used to form pathways, one must always consider their compatibility with the site. Crushed shell material may be a more suitable alternative.

Grassland Management

Given the low nutrient status of the sand pastures forming the semi-roughs and roughs, it may indeed not be necessary to carry out more than an annual inspection of these areas, checking for invasive broad-leaved weeds, scrub or other undesirable changes that may be occurring with gradual nutrient enrichment. In other, more inland areas where humus is building within the soil profile, it may be necessary to cut infrequently so as to maintain the botanical diversity and richness of these habitats. Cutting should be undertaken once or twice each year, possibly during August/early September, followed by the collection and removal of litter. A second cut during early March would be beneficial in suppressing any invading undesirable productive weeds, so effectively opening the sward for the main flowering period until the final late summer/early autumn cut. Once again, litter collection and removal must be enforced.

Other Considerations

Reseeding of Dune Grasslands

The links or dune grasslands constitute those areas of relatively flat land in between the seaward dunes and the landward scrub/tree vegetation. The native vegetation of these areas can become eroded and it may on occasion be necessary to reseed using native turfgrass species. This may prove successful providing that in any year the areas are not inundated by more than 2-3 cm of blown sand. Normally, the sand will need very little preparation other than to smooth out any high spots and obvious hollows.

Possibly, the most appropriate periods for seed establishment would be April/May and late August/September Earlier than these times, salt spray may be a particular problem, drought problems may also be acute later in the year. These limitations will be less important as the site becomes more sheltered.

The dune pastures tend, in the main, to support a relatively high pH together with a rich diversity of flowering plant species. Given the relative instability of the soil structure, reinstating the species content can be quite difficult. The most practical method may be to produce a stable ground cover, albeit relatively thin, relying on natural processes over a period of years to reinstate a more indicative vegetation type. In the first instance therefore, a total red fescue seeds mixture would be appropriate. However, further inland, consideration may be given to the inclusion of browntop bent, smooth-stalked meadow-grass, etc.

The red fescue is relatively slow-growing and drought-tolerant and sea-marsh selections, for example 'Dawson', have some tolerance to salt. Perennial ryegrass can produce a rapid ground cover, and may persist in spite of drought, but this species is never compatible with the natural links sward. It is totally unsuitable for use on links fairways where its tufted, upright habit and tough seed stalks make it unsatisfactory from both the playing and visual viewpoint. Even on pathways it should be used with caution since in that situation it will set seed and may spread into other sensitive areas of the course. In more nutrient-rich areas, possibly with a higher water retention, *Agrostis* species may be preferred.

Smooth-stalked meadow-grass is a common dune pasture grass species and, being relatively slow to establish, will not severely impede the growth or establishment of the finer-leaved fescues. Legumes such as *Lotus* and *Trifolium* play a vital role in the development of swards in nutrient-poor environments by fixing atmospheric nitrogen which can then be used by the principal grasses.

Adjacent to areas of ecological/botanical significance, the above seeds mixture may be undesirable as some of the sown grasses may invade and colonise the surrounding areas. It may be more appropriate to collect seed locally, assuming a sufficient area of land is available, although this is a relatively laborious and time-consuming task. Germination and establishment can be very slow on sand, and this can be helped by the careful and cautious use of fertilizers, with the aim here being to provide a constant source of nutrient rather than building up any excess reserves. Given the drought sensitivity of these areas, it is important to bury the seed to between 1 and 4 cm down and into more optimum moisture conditions. An appropriate seeding rate would be 18 to 28 g/ m^2 ($^1/_2$ to $^3/_4$ oz. per sq.yd.). Many of the failures in dune pasture reseeding tend to occur as a result of failure to keep established seedlings correctly nourished. Dune soils, by their nature, are deficient in potash and phosphate, as well as the highly mobile nitrogen. The initial fertilizer treatment may include a single application of 18 g/m^2 of an NPK 4:10:10 supplemented at appropriate intervals thereafter, perhaps on a bimonthly basis, with a similar low nitrogen product. Soil chemical analysis would provide a more accurate fertilizer programme.

Sand Stabilisation by Spraying
A number of products are available which may be sprayed on a soil to bind the surface temporarily, acting as protection against wind or water erosion. Soil stabilisers may be used to prevent wind erosion on exposed

dune areas or other sandy areas seeded with turfgrasses. Whilst seeding using turfgrass species as outlined previously will, without doubt, be the most cost-effective, there may on occasion be cause for considering one of the proprietary soil stabilisers. Stabilisers can be classified as glues or mulches having a cohesive nature helping to bind the sand particles. The stabiliser, once applied, must be sufficiently strong to withstand wind-blown rain, sand, seashells, etc. and must be flexible enough to move with the unstable sand below, so offering continued protection over relatively long periods. Once damaged, the stabilised surface will become less effective as the hole enlarges and wind and rain erosion continues. Stabilisers can be used in reseeding programmes and may be effectively applied by Hydroseeding, scan-seeding or spraying. The technique adopted will vary depending upon the relative position with respect to exposure and may be effective for 12 to 36 months.

In certain circumstances, seed germination can be improved by the use of a stabiliser as these can help to increase water retention. However, on sand where lack of moisture is the norm, water entry, germination and establishment can all be restricted due to the possible waterproofing nature of the materials used. Seed must always be buried well into the sand and the sand firmed before applying the stabiliser.

Seed must always be buried well into the sand before applying the stabiliser as germination is likely to be markedly reduced if the water-proof coat contacts with the seed.

Application must be such to form a glued crust of between 2 and 10 mm depth with sufficient pore space in between to allow relatively free percolation of water. Stabilisers can be spray-applied using a hand spray lance or similar during calm, dry periods, working backwards so as to avoid the need to disturb treated areas.

Dune Regeneration
In cases where public access has damaged dune faces, especially on the seaward side, some means of rebuilding the sand will be essential if the damaged areas are not to be extended by wind blow or high spring tides. In such circumstances, the majority of conservation agencies are generally opposed to hard engineering, i.e. gabions, rock rip-rap and/or groins, etc., due to their artificiality and the way in which the sea may undercut or work around them.

In general, it is better to rebuild dunes naturally, allowing wind blown sand to accumulate. To achieve this, some check to the wind will be vital and may involve the use of brushwood with stakes, second-hand chestnut paling fencing or plastic windbreak materials to catch and hold the wind-carried sand. Once the profile has been roughly formed, marram or sea lyme grass can be lifted from selected areas of the course and planted so as to further restabilise the dune face.

PLATE 22. Sand stabilisation using marram grass (*Ammophila arenaria*).

2.4 GRASSLANDS:
THEIR DEVELOPMENT AND MANAGEMENT

Rationale for Management
Traditional grasslands, including meadows and pastures, were once commonplace throughout the British landscape, affording wildlife with a considerable and varied habitat resource.

PLATE 23. Orange tip butterfly (*Anthocharis cardamines*) feeding on red campion (*Silene dioica*).

Since 1947 over 90% of our species-rich grasslands have been destroyed through land modification or destruction and today further threats, including inappropriate management or management neglect, may jeopardise the future of our remaining fragmented grassland heritage.

Grassland type and quality varies considerably, ranging from the monotonous amenity grasslands within the parkland areas of our towns and cities to those highly diverse and species-rich grasslands of the calcareous, chalk or limestone-rich downlands and heathlands to the acidic heaths and moors, to the semi-natural grasslands represented along roadside verges, railway embankments and the marginal land integral with the arable farming network.

All grasslands owe their existence to the early deforestation activities of man, together with the ongoing grazing effects of animals, principally rabbits, sheep, cattle, etc. On the golf course, these primary factors have, in the majority of cases, been removed (a possible exception being the common land golf course) leading to either over-tidying with the complete removal of the semi-natural grassland habitat or a total cessation of management leading to a build up of nutrients and a lack of species diversity and interest. Many golf courses do leave areas of grassland for wildlife, only in time to remove these completely as concern and criticism from members intensifies. Some management will be essential both to retain or improve the ecological significance of the grasslands represented on golf and to improve these areas in line with the requirements and objectives of the game.

Problems Encountered
The grasslands, particularly the deeper roughs (normally neglected), are subject to change and, without any form of upkeep or management, will undergo a continual process of succession, this being initiated by the relaxation or cessation of management and the build up of nutrients through leaf litter deposition leading to an increase in competitive grass and herb weed species and a loss of overall sward diversity. Continued succession will lead to a tussocky, unkempt sward with patches of scrub invading at intervals which may eventually spread to form dense and impenetrable thickets. Gradually, naturally regenerating trees may establish to form an incipient woodland within a relatively short period of time. Management must therefore be geared to halting this succession.

Over-tidying is the other extreme normally encountered on golf courses. Many areas are cut at fairly regular intervals, often quite unnecessarily. This not only leads to a lack of ecological quality and wildlife interest but does generate real concern from the general public and other non-statutory wildlife organisations. Moreover, this scenario does place an unwarranted burden on the greenkeeper's time and resource. True grassland roughs must be redefined, reinstated and managed according to their position and sward type.

Management Objectives
From the above, there is a clear need to strike a reasonable balance between how much management is given to halt natural succession and how much will be needed to satisfy the concerns of members and the problem of retrieving stray balls.

From an ecological perspective, whilst lack of management will reduce the botanical diversity, it may positively encourage certain ground nesting birds and some insect types.

Infrequent management may result in an increased botanical diversity, an increase in grassland butterflies and other insects, and will offer a visually acceptable feature to the golfer. Obviously, the position of the grassland and its function with respect to golf will be fundamental in determining any management strategy.

Given the variety of constraints as outlined above, it may be worth considering:

[a] developing an overall structural diversity, i.e. of different cutting heights and densities through the roughs;
[b] leaving some areas altogether (possibly areas in difficult corners or behind effective screenings, e.g. woodlands);
[c] the frequency of cut;
[d] the timing of any cutting operation.

Obviously, the above will in part be governed by the overall size and fragmentation of the roughs. Small areas may be more appropriately represented by adopting just one ongoing management technique, possibly two cuts per annum and all litter collected, but this will ultimately depend upon the sward type desired and/or encouraged.

Management Prescription
Grazing
Grazing is unparalleled in its benefits in the management of semi-natural grasslands and should continue as the major force driving the ecology of any grassland. Certainly on the common land golf clubs, natural grazing will do much to maintain the relatively high ecological and scientific significance but this management tool on a golf course is not without problems. Rabbits, sheep, cattle and horses can cause significant damage to putting surfaces.

Cutting
Cutting will inevitably be the most practical option available to the golf greenkeeper. In general, the majority of plant species will tolerate and adapt to this management regime. Much will be dependent upon the timing of cutting and the frequency of operations. It may be that in the first year or so of implementing any cutting programme an obvious decline in certain species is noted. With time, however, a more acceptable balance should develop, offering a reasonable degree of richness and diversity.

The success of the ongoing cutting programme will be dependent upon several factors, including quality and age of the sward, soil type and also whether litter is returned or removed. Leaving cut vegetation can in many cases smother the underlying sward, preventing light penetration and photosynthesis. Nutrients will also be returned to the grass/soil system.

PLATE 24. Enhanced visual interest through grading the cutting heights from fairway to rough.

The relative importance of the above factors will depend upon the quality and type of vegetation, the state of the returned material (whether fine clippings or a thick swathe) and indeed the existing nutrient status of the stand and time of year when cut.

It may be possible in certain calcareous grasslands, particularly those with thin skeletal soil profiles (the rendzinas of the downlands for example), to return cut material providing that it is presented in a finely divided form.

General guidelines for the cutting of fairways, semi-roughs and the adjacent roughs are well documented – normally 13-20 mm for fairways and 37-50 mm for semi-roughs. Even at these heights, it is possible to encourage a reasonable sward diversity as many perennial and rosette-forming annuals are able to tolerate frequent and fairly close defoliation. Usually, the removal of a flower, as distinct from the leaves, will encourage energy channelling into vegetative growth which may offer a more robust vegetation community.

On the drought-prone downs and alkaline grasslands normally supporting freely draining rendzinas where growth does tend to be inherently slow, cutting may be geared to maintaining tidiness rather than removing large amounts of vegetation. Here, cutting may be geared

PLATE 25. Cutting the roughs: an infrequent but essential operation.

to a single treatment on a one or two week basis with the cutting blades raised slightly so as to protect the ground-hugging species.

Roughs immediately in play may be maintained at a height of around 75 mm, although here actual heights of cut will be influenced by the severity of the hazard, the tightness of fairways and the degree of difficulty demanded at any particular hole. Similarly, minimising maintenance and maintaining a reasonable throughput of play will also be important considerations.

Deeper roughs out of immediate play should not be neglected. Infrequent cutting will be necessary to reduce the vigour of the more actively growing and productive weedgrasses which would otherwise suppress the slower growing, longer lived perennials. The actual frequency of cutting will largely be governed by the type of grass sward and its vigour. Fertile sites may need a minimum of four and a maximum of seven cuts per annum with all clippings being removed. Lower fertility grasslands may benefit from between one and four cuts per year with at least some finely divided clippings being returned.

A number of golf clubs are now considering two cuts to be an optimum. The first cut in the spring, possibly during mid March, under favourable ground and climatic conditions would be effective in removing early

PLATE 26. Common spotted orchid (*Dactylorhiza fuchsii*) within the rough.

productive growth and in suppressing its vigour sufficiently to allow the desirable components to flower and set seed before being overtaken by the faster growing weed species. A second cut during early August, i.e. upon completion of seed set, will be required to reinstate a more acceptable height of cut and further suppress the vigour of the undesirable weed species. Each cut may reduce the height of the sward to between 50 and 75 mm (2 and 3 in.). This cutting programme will offer an acceptably low height of cut over at least seven months of the year, with the height only exceeding 75 mm for between four and five months during March to early August. Given this approach, a maximum sward height may be in the region of 300 mm (12 in.) depending upon the nature of the grassland.

Apart from the obvious ecological benefits, i.e. the increased sward diversity and attractiveness to butterflies and other wildlife, such a

76

commitment to infrequent cutting may be much more acceptable to members, increasing the overall visual quality of the course without severely restricting play.

Other Considerations
Mowing Equipment
The range of mowing equipment available for cutting the different areas of the golf course is vast. This may include the conventional cylinder or reel mowers which use a scissor-like cutting action and may involve the petrol-driven or diesel tees-type mowers to the self-propelled/trailed three, five or seven unit gangs up to 6.25 metres (20.5 ft.) wide. These, in the main, are designed to work within shorter grass and will produce a relatively high quality finish. Cutting speed can be maintained independent of ground speed, and ground contours can be closely adhered to using the floating heads. The tractor-mounted hydraulic gangs are advantageous in that they do not tie up a tractor indefinitely but a major disadvantage can be that the majority of hydraulic gangs being used have no facility for fitting collecting boxes.

A variety of rotary and flail mowers are available, either self-propelled or tractor-mounted. These tend to smash the vegetation and can generally handle long, dense and tangled material. The cut material may be distributed as dense swathes with the rotary mower and this can smother the underlying sward. The recently introduced compact tractor trailed flails, including the vertiflail/scarifiers, are extremely useful both for light or heavy scarification, cutting (to variable heights) and for collecting cut material. Indeed, these machines can be used for other associated treatments, i.e. heather management, fairway scarification and leaf and litter collection.

Creating Flower-rich Grasslands
Flower-rich grasslands can offer a variety of interest, visual colour and, if created using naturalistic techniques, may increase the overall ecological significance of an otherwise relatively featureless site. If consideration is being given to enriching existing grasslands, an initial ecological appraisal should be undertaken so as to evaluate the existing botanical composition and species richness. This indeed may, or may not, be particularly obvious from a brief casual inspection and may, in part, be suppressed due to the past management strategies or indeed past neglect. Quite often, a change in management policies can result in a significant change in botanical diversity and interest.

Creating wild flower-rich meadows on new "bare" land acquired for the golf course may at first appear an attractive option, but there may be a number of practical problems that must be considered and overcome.

Developing Existing Grasslands

The fertility of any site is a major determining factor as to whether a grass/wild flower sward can be successfully established. Established grass leys tend to support moderate fertility levels when compared to bare arable land and can usually be further developed.

Following the initial ecological appraisal and providing that the perceived change in management would not be of detriment to the established sward, then consideration could be given to sowing a wild flower seed mixture.

The first operation would usually be to carry out a series of chemical soil analyses to determine the chemical status of the soil. High fertility can normally only be reduced by rather drastic measures, i.e. topsoil stripping, reversing the soil profile or by allowing the sward to flower, cutting before seed set, with concomitant collection and removal of litter so as to gradually reduce the nutrient status of the soil. It may be necessary to continue this operation over several years if a significant reduction is to be observed. These options would be rarely practical on the golf course and the club may, given very high fertility levels, be better advised to consider other appropriate naturalistic featuring.

pH can be adjusted relatively easily using either calcium carbonate (lime), flowers of sulphur or aluminium sulphate, depending upon individual requirements of the site.

Surface Preparation

Having achieved an acceptable nutrient/pH balance, surface preparation can commence.

[a]   Cutting: It will be necessary to cut the sward to a height of 25-50 mm (1-2 in.). The actual height will largely be determined by levels and the tussocky nature of the sward. All litter must be collected and discarded.

[b]   Create gaps in the sward: The next stage will be to thin the sward via intensive scarification using a heavy duty flail/scarifier, a tractor-drawn scarifier unit or similar. Several passes in different directions would be necessary, with the blades set to cut deeply into the surface thatch and fibre so as to create a relatively thin and open sward. The associated litter collected must be removed on completion of this work.

[c]   Seed choice: Although there are many different proprietary wild flower seed mixtures on the market, it is important to select the

right mix, i.e. one that meets existing site conditions, is complementary to the indigenous flora/vegetation of the area and one which is suitable to the constraints and objectives required by golf. Complex species mixtures and rarities should be avoided, their overall success may be limited due to the differing habitat specificities, greater problems of establishment, increased cost and increasing artificiality. Simple species mixtures guided by local conditions and established vegetation are more likely to survive.

Sowing
Autumn sowing is preferred as at this time the soil is generally moist and warm. The seed should be drilled into the surface using appropriate seeding equipment. Slot seeding has shown to be successful, although in dense swards the wild flowers may be swamped by the adjacent grasses. Slug problems have also proved problematic in some instances and must be considered. Other alternatives would include the precision drills and the rotary strip seeders. Both have proved particularly effective in recent trials carried out by English Nature. A suitable seeding rate for wild flowers without the associated grasses would be between 2 and 4 kg/ha and this would need bulking up with sand so as to facilitate spreading.

Aftercare
Watering may be important should drought conditions ensue after sowing, although the established grass sward should contribute positively in moisture retention and protecting the sward from exposure. The majority of flowers may have a vernalisation requirement and will not therefore germinate until the following spring period.

The management given during the first season will largely dictate the success or failure of the project. Regular cutting will be essential in reducing the vigour of the highly competitive perennial weeds. Thus, in the first season the first blooms should be ignored in favour of a regular cutting programme.

Delaying or ignoring cutting in the first growing season may result in the sward becoming overgrown and smothered to the loss of the desirable sward. Cutting should be carried out fairly frequently and should be dictated by growth of the sward. A cut could be made each time the herbage reaches an excess of 150 mm (6 in.), cutting back to around 50 mm (2 in.). All clippings must be removed and discarded. Cutting may be reduced with time to a more acceptable frequency. The number of cuts in any given season will, if sustained over time, largely dictate the quality of the sward and its composition.

PLATE 27. Cowslips (*Primula veris*) adjacent the tee.

Creating Wild Flower Grassland on Bare Soil

A number of courses have been or are extending into arable land, possibly with a view to lengthening the course at one or more holes, or to develop a whole new golf facility.

Wild flower grasslands can, in certain circumstances, form attractive golf features providing that:

[a] they complement and fit in with the rest of the course, and this will largely be governed by the type of course and whether the existing roughs are botanically species-rich;

[b] fertility levels are moderate to low.

On high fertility soils, unless the topsoil can be stripped (and possibly

80

sold) or mixed with sufficient subsoil to lower the nutrient status to an acceptable level, or if a nurse agricultural crop cannot be sown over two or even three years to be harvested before seed maturation, then the project would best be abandoned and other alternatives considered.

Ground Preparation
Given moderate to low nutrient status, surface preparation can commence. The first operation through the first season should be to lightly cultivate on occasion, following this work with chemical weed control treatments to fully eradicate the majority of surface weeds. Stone collection and the removal of boulders would also continue throughout the first growing season. By the early autumn a smooth, firm seed bed should be produced.

Choice of Species
Choice of species will reflect the site conditions, i.e. soil type, nutrient status, pH, trampling pressure and relative heights of species. The species mixture must be compatible with and a regular component of the surrounding grassland community. The species selected should be relatively abundant, enjoying a fairly wide natural distribution. They should be perennial, long-lived and preferably with a vegetative means of spread.

Colourful flowers add interest to the golf course and to visiting insects and may be included. The highly competitive species supporting single species stands in the wild should be avoided. The seed must have a high germination potential over a range of temperatures.

Sowing
Autumn sowings are preferred, germination being favoured by warm, moist soil conditions. Although seed rates vary from supplier to supplier, recommended rates may be the selection of an 80/20 or 90/10 grass/ wild flower seeds mix to be sown at a rate of between 30 and 35 kg/ha. These rates are quite low compared to the more general rates recommended for playing and putting surfaces. The wild flower grassland should consist of a relatively open sward with sufficient initial flowers and desirable grass species to encourage their natural spread. Dense swards are not desired due to the possibility of more aggressive species smothering and excluding the subordinate grasses and flowers within the grassland.

Aftercare will involve the careful use of the mowing equipment, cutting as frequently as is necessary, especially in the first year, so as to reduce the overall vigour of the more competitive species. Litter must be collected following each cut. An appropriate cutting frequency for the first year would involve a single cut each time the vegetation exceeds 150 mm in height, cutting back to a minimum of 50 mm. Thereafter, cutting may be reduced and geared to a more practical frequency of between four and seven cuts, with further reductions thereafter to between two and four cuts depending upon the sward type and botanical composition.

PLATE 28. Common blue (*Polyommatus icarus*), a common butterfly of alkaline grasslands.

2.5 WATER FEATURES:
THEIR DEVELOPMENT AND MANAGEMENT

Rationale for Management

Sometimes we have too much and sometimes too little, but one thing that cannot be denied is that water is important to all of us. This is no less true on the golf course where water plays an important role in turf maintenance. The management of water resources is therefore fundamental to the successful development and maintenance of any course.

Courses with their own natural water resources in the form of streams, lakes, ditches or ponds have an extremely valuable asset which, if properly developed and managed, can both enhance the golfer's environment whilst making a significant contribution to the conservation of the area as a whole.

As well as utilising natural water bodies, it is also possible to develop new water features on those courses which may not be as fortunate. If necessary, reservoirs can be developed purely for irrigation purposes but, in the right situation, water storage can be combined with the development of an attractive water feature. Such a development should not be undertaken lightly if it is to be successful.

PLATE 29. An attractive hazard and feature with considerable ecological interest.

83

Problems Encountered
The main problems resulting from poor or inadequate management include:

[a]   Loss of water quality through nutrient build up or contamination.
[b]   Loss of habitat and conservation value.
[c]   Inefficient usage of water resources for irrigation purposes.

Management Objectives
To maintain an attractive functional hazard high in conservation interest.

This will involve management aimed at the maintenance of water quality together with improving structural diversity and a variety of habitat types. A balance will need to be maintained between the extent of open water and that covered by vegetation as well as the amount of vegetation that can be maintained around the pond margin given the priorities for ball retrieval and the general aesthetics of the feature.

Where possible, valuable existing habitat features should be incorporated into the design from the outset and protected from further change. Habitats should be created to compensate for habitat losses elsewhere on the course and to improve the landscape and wildlife potential of the course. Any management must be appropriately phased so as to avoid disturbance at sensitive times of the year.

Management Prescription
The first step must be to assess the condition of the water at intervals, building up an appropriate management plan which recognises both the conservation value of the pond and the potential damage that can arise through mismanagement. The function and other requirements of the water feature, i.e. its use for irrigation, etc., must also be taken into account.

Written into the management programme will be the need to minimise archaeological and ecological damage. This may involve the careful use of any machinery so as not to alter the pond's profile or design.

Desilting
With time, leaf litter from overhanging trees and the pond vegetation will accumulate within the base of the pond and sediment from surface run-off, inlet ditches, etc. will gradually reduce the overall depth of the water feature and may lead to a dramatic change in the vegetation around the margins. Similarly, the decomposition of the organic material can lead to an oxygen deficit and an increase in nutrient status, lowering

the water quality and, in some instances, resulting in the death of aquatic life. Desilting may be required on a 10 to 15 year basis. This will involve dredging using an excavator, such as a 360° machine on tracks with a wide ditch cleaning bucket. The silt can be loaded into a dumper for carting away. It may be necessary to allow the silt to dewater before it can be disposed of. Alternatively, soft silt may be removed using a pump, this being particularly effective and, indeed, the only option in water features lined with a flexible butyl or similar liner.

Dredging or desilting can be catastrophic in some circumstances and a full assessment of the water body should be undertaken before such works are implemented. Where a pond has become largely infilled and has reached a relatively stable late successional stage, severe dredging to reinstate an open body of water can eliminate valuable diverse communities. In some instances, it may be more appropriate (and, indeed, cheaper) to allow a natural change towards the next successional stage as the pond gradually infills. Sensitive management may, however, be appropriate to maintain the water feature in its mid-successional stage.

PLATE 30. Regular management of the bank sides is vital if succession is to be halted.

Vegetation Management
On the golf course, leaving the marginal and bank side vegetation to choke the pond may not be acceptable and it will therefore be necessary to create a balance between the amount of open water and bank side

PLATE 31. Management neglect will encourage succession, leading to the loss of the "open" water feature.

vegetation. Before undertaking any vegetation clearance works, a full appraisal of the plant species present must be implemented as many quite rare species and communities worth preserving may have colonised. Substantial groupings of appropriate plant species can provide a range of major habitat type for a variety of pond animals. The more open water, being much more exposed, is dangerous to species which are liable to be preyed on. Many species, such as the dragonflies, depend upon bank side vegetation for completion of their life cycle. Whilst some species tend to use the flower heads of certain species, others may use the roots or stems, and whilst some like quite open swards, other species prefer quite dense and large groupings. It is therefore impossible to prescribe the ideal amount of plant cover for any given water feature, each grouping of plant species will inevitably support their own individual animal community. In the broader sense, more plant cover is likely to be better than less, although given the aesthetic and other requirements of the golf course, it will be essential that an appropriate balance is maintained.

Mechanical excavation is an option preferred on larger water courses but may be less suitable for the smaller ponds. Here, digging, cutting or raking could be employed and would be less harmful to the associated wildlife.

Chemical weed control also has particular value in some instances and should be used in conjunction with other basic physical approaches.

Timing
As with the other management practices discussed throughout this book, it will be imperative that the works programme recognises the need to phase the management operations over an appropriate time period. Indeed, cutting the water feature arbitrarily into appropriate portions, i.e. fifths, will help to minimise ecological damage and will enable the greenstaff to complete the required works within the time period allocated. Dredging and vegetation clearance works are best executed during a favourable period between September and late November so as to avoid the main breeding seasons of the fish, amphibians, insects (including dragonflies), etc. Management carried out during inappropriate periods of the year can have a catastrophic effect, killing wildlife and destroying valuable breeding sites. Disturbance in winter can severely stress or kill aquatic life due to the adverse temperature of the surface water and at this time many species hibernating or lying semi-dormant within the silt bed would be killed by desilting operations.

Phasing of the management work will involve clearing or thinning one or two areas of the pond on an annual basis. Under no circumstances should the whole of the water feature be cleared at any one time.

PLATE 32. Algae prefer periods of calm, sunny weather.

87

Algae
At certain times of the year, usually after periods of wind disturbance, followed by periods of calm, sunny weather, algae can become prolific as the nutrient levels rise towards the surface. Physical dredging and netting are the main ways of controlling this problem, though these may need to be repeated throughout the main growing period on several occasions to be fully effective. Alternatively, chemical control may be considered, although this could have an adverse effect on other desirable plant species. At the time of writing, both terbutryne and diquat are approved for algal control in slow-moving water bodies.

Other methods would involve using bank side vegetation to reduce nutrient movement into the water body or the use of barley straw to immobilise phosphate.

Reeds planted around the margin of a pond or other water feature may be effective in capturing nutrients. Bacteria surrounding the roots and rhizomes, whilst utilising oxygen produced by the roots, may be effective in breaking down and thus immobilising nutrients, so reducing their concentrations before they enter the water body. Although, at the time of writing, this work is being centred around the treatment of sewage, it may in the future have considerable application in a broader sense for the control of pollution in ponds on golf courses.

Similarly, loose barley straw applied to ponds during the early spring period has been shown to be effective in controlling or preventing algal blooms before algal growth starts. The straw itself has a low phosphate concentration and is able to decompose and lock up phosphate within the general body of the water, so rendering it unavailable to the algae. The straw will indirectly provide an excellent source of food for other pondlife, so increasing the health and overall productivity of the water feature. Current recommendations suggest ten conventional straw bales per 4,000 m^2 of surface area as an optimum application rate, though this, with future research, may be revised.

Water Features Design and Construction
Siting
One of the first considerations must be to determine just what can be achieved in any given area. Whilst a small individual water feature on part of one hole may have a very limited impact on the overall layout, a much larger feature will inevitably involve a greater number of holes, so influencing the layout and possibly the whole character of the course. A pond or lake can transform an otherwise mediocre hole, introducing an attractive strategic hazard.

The initial site assessment must take due consideration of the existing vegetation characteristics as well as the general topography of the site. Care should be taken when planning a new pond not to destroy existing areas of high wildlife or archaeological interest. Water flow will also play a major part in dictating the location of a water feature in relation to the surrounding topography. Larger water features can be elevated, though careful consideration must be given to their construction and final appearance. Thoughtful design and development within an area of low lying land will produce a feature which looks natural and fits in with the landscape.

The catchment to the site must be taken into account in order to establish the quantity of water available to maintain summer water levels. Ideally, the watercourse will supply all of the water needed for irrigation and the natural evaporation losses. Indeed, up to 450 mm depth of water could be lost from the surface of a lake due to evaporation in the southern areas of the country. In drought periods this can reduce a potentially attractive feature into a muddy depression. In some situations, the only source of water available is surface run-off and flow from underground drainage systems. With the dry summers of the early 1990s, much greater emphasis has been placed on the harvesting of water in an attempt to reduce the demand on other water sources for irrigation. The catchment area and yield of water will need to be carefully evaluated and, in many instances, it may be necessary to top-up water levels from other appropriate sources, i.e. mains or borehole.

If water levels are raised by the construction of the water feature, the effects on drainage must be considered. Where gradients are steep, the effects on the drainage may be localised and easily overcome. In flatter situations, higher water levels could affect a much larger area, possibly exacerbating already poor drainage conditions. Good drainage outlets must be maintained for all drainage systems.

In choosing a location for a lake, the available space must be taken into account. Is it possible to achieve the volume of water required for irrigation? Where substantial earthworks are needed, is there sufficient space available to accommodate embankments without producing an artificial "engineered" formation? Numerous attempts at creating attractive water features have failed due to a lack of appreciation as to just how much space is required.

Design
First and foremost, it will be necessary to achieve a natural appearance

so as to fit the water feature into the landscape rather than imposing the feature upon it. It would be worth studying other semi-natural features within the area to gain a more full appreciation of their character and form. Indeed, a tarn in the upland areas would be very different in form from a larger water body in a lowland situation.

Introducing any lake or pond, however simple the design, onto a golf course will encourage some wildlife to the area. However, to achieve the maximum conservation benefit, the design should incorporate as many different features and habitats as possible. There will often be special considerations to take into account, such as abstraction of irrigation water (see Appendix III) and siting of pump housing, but there is no reason why conservation should not form a major part of the design process.

A section through a lake or pond will generally reveal a range of different habitats, from dry ground through to the shallow margins and deeper open water areas. It is better to avoid steep or uniform banks. An irregular shoreline with varying depth will be more interesting and provide more opportunities for creating the desired habitat types, so maximising conservation benefit. Generally speaking, a deeper lake will provide more stable conditions, shallow waters being much more susceptible to rapid fluctuations in both temperature and oxygen levels. Inevitably, some silting will occur, so reducing the overall depth in time, and this should be allowed for. In larger water features, the depth should reach 3 metres so as to maintain areas of open water. The soil type may influence the formation of banks. In sandy situations, watercourses can carry large quantities of sediment which could cause very rapid silting. It may be useful to form a stilling area to trap sediment which can then be removed without disturbing the main water body. Gently sloping banks and ledges up to 600 mm deep do tend to be the most important for wildlife conservation.

Other features to consider during the design stage would include services, adjacent roads, arable land and the presence of trees within and around the vicinity of the water feature. Roads can result in salt and other chemical run-off, all of which can reduce the water quality of the feature. Similarly, fertilizer run-off from arable land may be quite high, again influencing water quality. Leaf deposition from adjacent copses, woodlands, etc. can be quite substantial and will accelerate the silting process and may lead to stagnation in smaller ponds.

Construction
Construction of the water feature may involve total excavation, i.e. digging a hole and filling with water, or cut and fill which would involve

using spoil from the excavated hole to build and increase a retaining embankment. Although this is certainly much more economical with respect to water volume stored, it may in many instances appear far more artificial.

Soil type will be of particular importance,. A soil containing over 30% clay with the remainder being made up of a sand fraction of varying particle size distribution would be ideal, giving both impermeability and stability. Slopes to the banks should be varied, with falls in the order of 1 in 3 being optimum. Shelves and slopes extending between depths of 150 and 600 mm should be created, gradually extending to the deeper areas of the pond. An irregular shoreline will help to maximise the overall length of shoreline, as would islands, either natural or artificial. Ideally, the water feature should interconnect, at least in part, with the deeper rough so as to extend the bank side habitat and to act as a buffer between the in-play and ecological zones.

A number of lining materials are available and include:

[a] *Clay.* Raw clay puddled around the sides and bottoms of the water feature will, if relatively stone-free, form an impermeable seal. Puddled clay is, however, prone to cracking during periods of drought and repair would involve extensive repuddling. Cost is quite variable, being dependent largely upon transportation costs and whether a local source of the clay can be found.

[b] *Concrete.* Although concrete has been used to line water features, it is quite costly and can release toxic chemicals for long periods into the water body. Concrete may look somewhat unsightly on the golf course.

[c] *Butyl.* Butyl rubber has proved to be a very effective method of lining water features and is relatively cheap to purchase. A gauge of 0.75 mm would be the most commonly used. Butyl is sensitive to damage during its installation and it is essential that the base and sides are firm, smooth and free of sharp stones. Butyl is UV sensitive and will, in time, deteriorate unless it is adequately covered and protected.

Polythene sheeting can be reinforced but may not be as durable as butyl rubber.

Landscaping
Once constructed, small groupings of appropriate marginal and emergent plant species should be planted around the margin of the pond. Consideration must be given to the practicalities of their placement with

regard to both ball retrieval and the overall aesthetics of the project. Emergent species tend to be the larger rushes and irises, and these should be planted towards the back of the pond so as not to interfere with ball retrieval or views over the water feature. These species, including bulrush and yellow flag, would normally reach a height of between 1 and 2 metres. Marginal species, including marsh marigold, purple loosestrife and soft rush, may reach up to 300 mm in height and would be appropriate around the front and sides. All plants should be arranged in single species groupings and planted directly into the margin of the water body. Lilies would also be an attractive feature. Both the white pond lily and yellow lily are native and found growing naturally through the countryside. These could be planted directly into the water body at suitable locations and where the total depth is likely to exceed 60 cm (2 ft.).

Other Considerations

PLATE 33. A well managed ditch can be an attractive feature of the course

Ditches
Ditches on golf courses represent valuable linking systems, their linear nature offering a major connecting system which can act as a routeway for the distribution of plants and animals. Apart from the major ecological benefits, the ditch is also of major importance in drainage, with the major criteria being to ensure the rapid movement of water through and off the course. Many ditches tend to be quite artificial,

running in a linear, regimented fashion with very few obvious meanders and with very little thought to their vegetation featuring. These areas could be greatly improved given consideration to the following. The initial ditch design should be flexible incorporating natural meanders as appropriate to the site topography, together with wider sections, i.e. ponds or swales, so as to create further interest and to facilitate vegetation planting.

PLATE 34. Informal ditch contouring. Swales or pools offer scope for landscaping.

During excavation, provision should be made for varying the depth, possibly between 150 and 300 mm below general falls so as to ensure some water is held during periods of reduced flow. The bank sides should be shallow, not exceeding 1 in 3 so as to enable players to recover balls with relative ease and to create more gentle and natural slopes to the water's edge. Varying the width and depth of the ditch will add both to the aesthetics of the area and the physical diversity of the water feature, so maximising the colonisation potential from the wildlife perspective.

Trees, shrubs and other emergent vegetation planted appropriately along the length of the ditch would help to diversify the ecological interest whilst adding significant aesthetic appeal to the natural placement and position of the feature.

Ditches without some management input will become gradually over-grown, silted and eroded, requiring some attention to their reshaping, vegetative clearance and replanting. The vegetation management should be carried out on an infrequent, phased basis, working in stages along its length.

PLATE 35. Inappropriate management of ditches on the golf course will fuel public opposition, may adversely affect the ecology of the course and surrounding land and, through erosion and other management problems, will unnecessarily increase the workload of the greenstaff.

PART 3

FURTHER ENVIRONMENTAL CONSIDERATIONS

3.1 ENVIRONMENTAL CONSIDERATIONS IN THE USE OF FERTILIZERS AND PESTICIDES ON THE GOLF COURSE

One of the major concerns regarding the environmental impact of golf courses is the potential for transport of fertilizer nutrients and pesticides into ground water and adjacent watercourses. Nitrate from fertilizer and pesticide residues in ground water reserves pose a potential risk to human health. Fertilizer nitrate and phosphate inputs into watercourses lead to eutrophication with consequent damaging effects on aquatic animal and plant life. These will also be harmed by excessive concentrations of pesticide.

Research has been carried out, and continues to be carried out, on fertilizer and pesticide loss from golf green turf. The bulk of the research has taken place in the USA. In the USA, golf greens may receive relatively large amounts of fertilizer and pesticides and it is therefore perceived that excessive losses to the environment occur.

Fertilizer Run-off
In the few studies that have been undertaken, it has been reported that the amount of fertilizer nutrient lost from turf in surface water run-off is negligible. Linde *et al.* (1995) investigated nitrogen and phosphate run-off from creeping bentgrass and perennial ryegrass turf maintained as golf fairways on 9 to 11% slopes. Turf plots were treated with NPK fertilizer and irrigated within 24 hours. The run-off water was found to contain similar amounts of nitrogen and phosphate as the irrigation water indicating that little, if any, of the applied fertilizer was lost by run-off.

Fertilizer Leaching Losses
The main concern with regard to the loss of fertilizer nutrients through leaching from soils has been with regard to nitrate-nitrogen. Most investigations have therefore concentrated on nitrate. Reporting on a study carried out by Roy in Maryland on a recently constructed golf course, Petrovic (1994) noted that the conversion of the site from arable agriculture to a golf course resulted in a lowering of nitrate concentration in underlying ground water. In a survey of research on nitrogen leaching from applied fertilizer, it was reported that losses were generally far less than 10% of that applied (Petrovic, 1990).

A short term trial was carried out in the UK to look at leaching losses of phosphate and potassium, as well as nitrogen, in golf green turf growing on various rootzone mixes (Lawson & Colclough, 1991). The results showed that once dense turf cover was established, the concentration of nitrate leached to drainage was well below the European Community guideline for drinking water. The total amount of nitrogen leached represented no more than 2.6% of that applied (20 kg/ha of N per annum). However, when the amount of nitrogen applied to the turf was increased to an excessive level for fescue-bent turf (40 kg/ha of N per annum), the concentration of nitrate in drainage water was well above the EC guideline. The excess elution occurred mainly in late autumn.

The concentrations of phosphate in the leachate were extremely low, but were high for potassium. Indeed, more potassium was lost through leaching than applied in fertilizer.

The Use of Herbicides in Ecological Management of the Golf Course
The use of herbicides on golf courses is becoming an increasingly emotive and controversial issue. Indeed, in Western Europe herbicide use has been severely restricted or, as is the case in some areas, completely banned through the "tightening" of legislation. Herbicides are used, and indeed are vital, in the management of nature reserves and other highly emotive conservation areas. Like nature reserves, golf courses require active ecological management if they are to retain their characteristic flora and fauna. Physical control methods should always be preferred and the use of chemicals obviously restricted as there may indeed be some unintended side effects.

To reduce these side effects to an absolute minimum, one should always: choose the most selective herbicide available or, if possible, those offering direct application (paintbrush or similar); minimise spray drift by using coarser droplets; and not spray if the wind speed is any stronger than a light breeze. Check on the herbicide's potential for revaporisation "vapour drift" as these chemicals can revaporise from the target plants.

Because no herbicide is strictly selective, i.e. chemicals treating bracken will also kill rare and sensitive ferns, caution must be taken as to the most suitable product available, possibly to be used as a dribble rather than a fine spray and, if likely to vaporise, used only when temperatures are not likely to exceed 15°C (59°F).

Integral with the use of chemicals will be the need to consider the root cause of the problem and readjusting the management work to suit.

Pesticide Leaching
A survey of ground water under four golf courses in Cape Cod, USA found that, in the 12 pesticides studied, all were present in concentrations well below health guidance levels (Petrovic 1994).

Higher concentrations of pesticide were found in measurements made immediately below turf rootzones where high rates of irrigation had been applied soon after pesticide applications. Greater amounts of pesticide were leached where applied to immature, seedling turf, particularly on sandy soils.

Petrovic (1995) concluded that dense, healthy turf dramatically reduces the risk of pesticide leaching even on sand-based putting greens where there is a significant potential for leaching.

Conclusions
It is evident that, where applied at normal application rates for fine turf, the amounts of fertilizer lost through surface run-off or leaching are very small. The exceptions are on seed beds, turf beds or young, immature turf where a dense rooting system is not present to capture applied nutrients. The potential for nutrient leaching in such situations is increased by the free draining, sand-dominated rootzones in modern golf green constructions. Thus, slow-release fertilizer products should be used for pre-seeding, pre-turfing and application to immature turf.

For pesticides, the position would appear to be similar. On mature, dense turf there is less likelihood of leaching than on immature turf, particularly if growing on a sand-dominated rootzone. It is evident that caution is required in such situations.

The Use of Fertilizers in Through the Green Management
Through the greens, i.e. the fairways, semi-roughs, roughs and carries, do not generally require any form of NPK fertilizer. Indeed, the principal objective on the majority of golf courses should be working towards reducing the chemical status to an acceptable minimum sufficient to retain sustained growth of the finer-leaved grasses and associated desirable wild flowers.

The invasive or competitively aggressive weedgrasses to fulfil their life cycle require a relatively high and constant nutrient resource. Although, in the main, the majority of grasslands do support rather high fertility levels, there may be on occasion a requirement to add an appropriate fertilizer/soil ameliorant, possibly on a localised basis and only to fairway areas. Regular use, however, even on fairway areas will only serve to encourage undesirable coarse grass growth.

If applied with care, local applications of nitrogen can help the recovery of localised areas such as carries, approaches, etc.

On the more sandy and freely draining fairways, there may on occasion be a requirement to add an appropriate soil ameliorant or possibly an organic-type top dressing locally to help relieve drought stress, and possibly seaweed extract-type products or trace minerals may be used to stimulate soil micro-organisms on the recovery of grass growth.

When using any organic ameliorants or NPK fertilizers on fairways, carries, adjacent any area of grassland or other habitat of high ecological significance, great care must be taken with respect to how and when to apply the product and with what equipment. Care must also be taken not to encourage drifting of the product into the more sensitive areas.

3.2 SPECIFIC PROBLEMS

Management of Mammals and Birds
Rationale for Management
A number of mammal and bird species, such as rabbits, badgers, Canada geese and moles, may have to be managed by greenkeepers when they cause problems on golf courses. Of these animals, the species which will probably cause most problems is the rabbit. Rabbit numbers are increasing as a result of the waning effects of myxomatosis. The disease now kills only about 20% of the population each year, compared to a literal 99.9% when it first arrived in the country in the early 1950s. Rabbits have developed genetic immunity to the disease and, in addition, strains of virus are now much weaker than the original ones. Eventually it may not kill any at all. Taking the country as a whole, the population is currently at about 30% of pre-myxomatosis levels and may well double in the future, although in some places numbers may have already returned to pre-myxomatosis levels. However, a new disease specific to rabbits called Viral Haemorrhagic Disease has recently (1992) arrived in this country to complicate this story. So far, most deaths which have been reported have been of show rabbits and, as far as is known, it has killed wild rabbits at fewer than ten locations. It is at present difficult to be precise about the course the disease may take but it is considered that populations will not be dramatically reduced in the long term, although there could be reductions lasting a couple of years. Therefore, problems with rabbits are still likely to increase.

Canada geese were introduced into the United Kingdom in the late 17th Century to the parks and gardens of stately homes but have since spread to other habitats, especially in the last 40 years. They are now widespread in England but more locally distributed in Scotland and Wales. The increase in sand and gravel extraction has, in particular, resulted in numerous disused water-filled pits and lakes which provide ideal habitats for this bird. Consequently, in the last 25 years the UK population has trebled from about 20,000 to 60,000 birds and may reach 120,000 by the end of the decade. Therefore, problems with Canada geese are also likely to increase.

Moles and badgers are not known to be increasing in numbers and therefore problems with these species are likely to remain at present levels.

Public attitudes to wildlife management are such that the welfare of wildlife is, quite properly, a major concern and therefore greenkeepers will have to manage these animals in a humane manner. There is also legislation in place which prescribes the way in which many animals can be managed, particularly, for example, badgers. The objectives of management programmes, the types of problem encountered and solutions to these problems, which take account of welfare and legal considerations, are outlined in the following sections.

Management Objectives
Wildlife on a golf course may be of considerable ecological importance and, in addition, may make a course more marketable to potential members as well as to existing members in terms of the course's aesthetic appeal. Therefore, the objectives must be to manage any species only when numbers increase to a level where they are causing economic losses to the course and then only to take such measures as necessary to reduce losses to non-economic levels. Every effort should therefore be made to quantify the costs of damage before deciding whether a management programme is necessary and to record the costs of the programme and to measure its effectiveness to ensure that it is cost-effective. Monitoring in this way will also enable determination of whether the programme needs to be changed and when it can be stopped.

Problems Encountered
The problems caused by these species are mainly to the turf of fairways, greens, tees or around bunkers. Rabbits dig burrows which are particularly prevalent on slopes and banks where drainage of water is more efficient. Digging occurs throughout the year but is more common in spring when new nesting sites are being dug in preparation for the birth of young. On flat ground, burrows are usually no more than 1 metre deep. Rabbits also cause damage by digging smaller, shallow scrapes in the soil which are considered to be a type of territorial marking or a means of obtaining access to plant roots on which to feed. Badgers damage turf by digging holes when looking for food, such as insect grubs or worms, and the most obvious damage which moles cause is the hills of soil produced as a result of digging their underground tunnel systems. These tunnels are 40-50 mm in diameter, can be several hundred metres long and can run at depths of up to 2 metres below the surface. Geese cause damage to the grass particularly around ponds and lakes on a golf course by excessive grazing and trampling or 'puddling' of the ground.

Other problems which may be encountered are newly planted young trees being damaged or killed by rabbits eating the bark or biting the tops off the trees and areas being made unplayable as a result of excessive fouling by geese. These droppings may also pose a potential health hazard if players eat, smoke or drink without washing their hands after handling golf balls which may have landed in them. In addition, during the nesting period geese may become aggressive towards members (although some greenkeepers may not see this as a problem!).

Management Solutions

Rabbits. Unfortunately, there is no simple solution to the problems caused by rabbits, although under the 1954 Pests Act it remains the legal obligation of occupiers of land to take steps to destroy wild rabbits on their land or, if this is not practical, to prevent rabbits from causing damage on adjoining land. There is a range of management methods which can be used. Numbers can be reduced by gassing rabbits in their burrows, by ferreting, trapping or shooting. A single gassing operation, using either a cyanide-based compound or a phosphine-based compound, has been found to reduce numbers by about 65%, whereas a single shooting or ferreting operation will reduce numbers by only 30%. Numbers are best reduced during late winter (November to March), usually by using a combination of these techniques, because rabbit numbers are at their lowest at this time of year due to natural mortality. Any action taken before winter will only replace rather than add to this mortality. Also, control at this time of year will reduce the breeding population before the next breeding season begins in January/February and therefore there will be fewer young around that year.

Non-lethal methods such as fencing can be used to exclude rabbits from parts of the course and, if properly maintained, can be over 90% effective. Repellents are also available which can be sprayed onto turf but data on the effectiveness of these compounds are at present limited. Finally, tree guards can be used to provide effective protection for individual trees.

Badgers. Badgers and their setts are protected by legislation in this country. The most recent of these Acts is the 1992 Protection of Badgers Act. The Acts make it an offence to interfere with badgers or their setts without a licence and preventing badgers causing damage is a complex problem which is too complicated to deal with in this type of publication. However, an extensive booklet for this purpose, called "Problems with Badgers?", is available from the RSPCA (Causeway, Horsham, West Sussex, RH12 1HG).

Canada geese. Canada geese are protected by the Wildlife and Countryside Act 1981 which requires that a licence must be obtained from the Department of the Environment or the Ministry of Agriculture, Fisheries and Food for certain types of management procedures and for any control carried out during the close season (February to August inclusive). These procedures include egg pricking, egg substitution and shooting during the close season or at night. However, the Act does not allow licences to be issued if the only purpose is to prevent damage to amenity land and therefore it is unlikely that one would be issued for management on golf courses.

Procedures not requiring a licence include fencing along the edge of ponds or lakes to deny easy access to adjoining grass. This may make an area less attractive to the birds and, consequently, may lead to a reduction in numbers. Also, altering the habitat by, for example, allowing the grass to grow or planting shrubs can be undertaken to break up the open vistas preferred by geese along the water's edge as this may also discourage them. Newly planted shrubs should, of course, be protected by fencing during establishment. Visual scarers can be used but, although they can be effective, they may be unacceptable on aesthetic grounds. Finally, shooting during the day (under licence) between September and January may be considered as a last resort but, as it has to be done during the day, it is unlikely that this would be accepted by members and, in addition, there may be safety problems.

Moles. Moles are managed mainly by poisoning, by gassing and by trapping. Poisoning is carried out by placing worms treated with strychnine in mole runs. However, the sale or supply of strychnine for general purposes is prohibited under the Pharmacy and Poisons Act 1933, exception being made in favour of persons with written authority from MAFF to purchase it for the express purpose of killing moles. Written authority will be given only to those who have received training in the technique and further information on how to obtain training can be obtained from MAFF offices. Treated worms should be placed in deep, rather than surface, runs to prevent them becoming a hazard to other wildlife. Gassing is conducted mainly by placing tablets which generate phosphine gas into their runs. Traps, which kill moles, should also be set in deep rather than surface runs and should not be set in mole hills. Traps are made by several manufacturers but are based on one or two principles. One type, the 'pincer' or 'scissor' trap has two pairs of spring loaded jaws which are kept apart by a trigger. The other traps the mole in a spring-activated wire loop which is particularly useful in light crumbly soil because the metal plate which is aligned with the roof of the mole run helps to prevent soil falling into the trap when the trap is covered. Control is best undertaken between October and April when moles tend to be most active and their workings easily seen.

APPENDIX I

REINSTATEMENT OF HEATHER ON THE GOLF COURSE USING PHYSICAL AND MECHANICAL METHODS

By R.S. TAYLOR[1], O. STEFANYSZYN[2] & P.M. CANAWAY[1]
[1]The Sports Turf Research Institute, Bingley, West Yorkshire BD16 1AU
[2]School of Biological and Earth Sciences, Liverpool John Moores University, Byrom Street, Liverpool L3 3AF

SUMMARY
Golf courses increasingly provide protection for diminishing wildlife resources including heath and moorland dominated by *Calluna vulgaris* (heather). Frequently, because of incorrect management, stands of *Calluna* become invaded by scrub or grasses, or may be allowed to degenerate with age. Two trials were undertaken on a golf course to compare different methods of reinstatement of *Calluna*. These entailed main plot treatments of: [1] scarification of the soil surface; [2] burning; [3] rotovation and sub-plot treatments comprising: [i] spreading of brashings (cut heather stems); [ii] spreading of heather capsules; [iii] spreading of capsules with a nurse grass mixture; [iv] leaving the surface bare. The results showed that of the main plot treatments, surface scarification was the most effective method of encouraging heather seedling establishment. Of the sub-plot treatments, leaving the surface bare and spreading of capsules with a nurse grass mixture were the most effective treatments. The implications of the results for reinstatement of heather on golf courses are discussed.

INTRODUCTION
Heath and moorland dominated by *Calluna vulgaris* (L.) Hull (ling or heather) throughout the British Isles is becoming increasingly fragmented. At the beginning of the 19th Century Britain supported over 50,000 hectares of viable heath (excluding moorland). This represented over a third of the European total (Anon. 1988). The intensification of farming, industry and other land uses has over the last 100 years led to a massive reduction in the total heathland area remaining. A number of land uses have been instrumental in securing large areas of the remaining heathland, these include common land, Ministry of Defence land and certainly a number of golf courses.

English Nature (formerly the Nature Conservancy Council) in a survey of 1,665 golf courses estimated from a total of 33,300 hectares of rough that around 3,600 was of the heathland type (180 courses). The moorland habitat represented on 90 golf courses examined occupied a total rough area of 1,800 hectares (Dair & Schofield, 1990).

The heather-dominated vegetation on the golf course represents a particularly favourable environment, offering excellent hazards as well as individual character and visual appeal. On a number of golf courses the heathland habitat is under severe pressure simply through neglect. The main management methods involved in maintaining habitat quality, i.e. burning and grazing, may have severe limitations in the golf environment. Grazing is still practised on a few golf courses built within common land where the rights of the commoners are still upheld. Burning, although practised on a number of courses, does have several severe limitations, not least is the difficulty in executing a successful burn at the right temperature under the right conditions.

The greenkeeper, therefore, must look to other techniques for heather reinstatement involving both physical and mechanical methods.

During the winter of 1991 the STRI set up two trials at the St Ives golf course, Bingley, West Yorkshire, whose object was to determine the best method of encouraging heather reinstatement.

Growth and Management of *Calluna*
Calluna vulgaris is a relatively short-lived evergreen shrub, normally associated with acidic, well drained soils. It is an important species of our heathlands and is certainly a dominant component of many established golf courses. Normally thought to display an upright habit, heather does, especially with age, become prostrate or horizontal with only the young terminal shoots ascending towards the available light.

During the early part of its life cycle, i.e. after germination, heather enters into an initial pioneer or establishment phase lasting around five years. This leads into a second very productive stage known as the building phase. This period of very active growth and concomitant increase in biomass may last over 15 years and it is during this time that the maximum increase in growth density and canopy spread will be noted. The plants through this period display a marked ability to regenerate vegetatively following repeated but infrequent cutting. Indeed, management at this time will help to retain the plant's juvenility indefinitely (Grime *et al.*, 1988).

If neglected over the next 10 years the plant will pass through the mature and degenerate stage, the stems tending to become woody. Individual branches grow away from the centre, leaving a bare, central zone and marked thinning of the canopy. Weed invasion at this time may increase, particularly within the central gaps. Cutting during the latter stages is unlikely to encourage vegetative regeneration.

MATERIALS AND METHODS

Two areas on the St Ives golf course, Bingley were selected for this study. These included areas of rough on the left of the 14th fairway and the left of the 10th/11th fairways. The main prerequisite for site selection included finding a relatively flat, uniform, stone-free surface away from the main areas of play and supporting the appropriate vegetative cover.

The nature of the experiment dictated that two very different sites be selected. The first (Trial A) was dominated by old, woody heather and the second (Trial B) consisted of predominantly coarse grass with patchy heather. *Molinea caerulea* and *Nardus stricta* were the main grass species.

The experimental treatments were as follows. Main plot treatments consisted of: [1] scarification (involving initial flailing of the heather to ground level, followed by scarification of the soil surface using a tractor-mounted vertiflail/scarifier); [2] burning; and [3] rotovation to 100 mm depth. Because of differences in the nature of the vegetation on the two trials, procedures for the scarification treatment (main plot) differed in some details.

In both trials growth was removed. In Trial A the ground was prepared by making a number of passes with a tractor-drawn vertiflail/scarifier (Amazone Groundkeeper). The underlying humus was exposed. In Trial B where tussocky and coarse grass dominated, the humus layer was exposed via a process of initial flailing, followed by sod cutting to a depth of 50 mm (2 in.). This was necessary to remove the surface fibre which had accumulated. Burning was carried out with the aid of a portable flame gun to produce a temperature of c. 400°C which was monitored using a pyrometer. In practice, difficulty was experienced in maintaining a consistent temperature, this falling below 400°C at times. Wind speed was light and therefore the burn was conducted downwind.

Rotovation was carried out using a pedestrian operated rotovator to 100 mm depth. Within each main plot, sub-plot treatments comprised:

Brashing: cut heather stems spread at a rate of 200 g m^{-2}
Capsules: the top 5 cm of the heather plants containing seed heads with seed, spread at a rate of 500 g m^{-2}
Capsules + capsules + nurse grass mixture sown at 15 g m^{-2} comprising:
        40% *Festuca rubra* L. spp. *commutata* Gaud. 'Cascade'
        20% *Agrostis capillaris* L. 'Tracenta'
        20% *F. ovina* L. 'Novina'
        20% *F. tenuifolia* Sibth. 'Barok'

Bare: no further treatment after initial surface preparation

Hence, the experiment consisted of a split plot design with four sub-plot treatments imposed on the three main plot treatments laid out in three randomised blocks. All treatments were applied on 14-15 March 1991.

Prior to application of the various treatments, seed capsules were collected by removing the top 5 cm of growth. These were used immediately in the subsequent experiments.

Three soil samples to 10 cm depth were also collected from each block, analysed thereafter for pH. The mean pH in both Trial A and Trial B was 3.9 ($\pm$ 0.28 in both cases). Samples were also collected from each main plot for estimation of the viable seed bank within the soil. An average of 1,749 ($\pm$ 36) viable seeds m^{-2} was found over the two trials.

Assessment of seedling regeneration was carried out from 23 July to 28 October 1992. The data were recorded using a 1 x 1 metre grid quadrat and the number of heather seedlings in each 10 cm^2 grid was counted and recorded.

The data were analysed using analysis of variance of the split plots model using GENSTAT statistical package. The data were subjected to $\log_{10}$ transformation prior to analysis and the back-transformed means are presented in the Results section.

RESULTS
Trial A
The results of seedling counts on the main plot treatments are given in Table 1 (back-transformed from the $\log_{10}$ means). The main treatments were significant at $p < 0.001$.

Scarification produced by far the greatest number of seedlings, differences between burning and rotovation being small in contrast.

TABLE 1
Effects of scarification, rotovation and burning on the number of heather seedlings (seedlings m^{-2})

Scarification	Rotovation	Burning (p = 0.05)	LSD
1011	54.8	88.1	1.83

For the sub-plot treatments (Table 2) there were also significant differences among treatments at p <0.05. Leaving the ground bare (following the main plot treatments) gave the highest population of seedlings, followed by spreading of capsules together with a nurse grass. Spreading of capsules without a nurse grass produced significantly fewer heather seedlings than the combined treatment, as did the spreading of brashings.

TABLE 2
Effects of sub-plot treatments (spreading brashings, heather capsules + nurse grass, spreading of heather capsules alone, or leaving the surface bare) on the number of heather seedlings (seedlings m^{-2})

Spread brashings	Capsules + nurse grass	Spread capsules	Left bare	LSD (p = 0.05)
85.9	232	126	330	2.45

Trial B
Counts of heather seedlings were carried as in Trial A, however, a large number of the plots showed no heather seedlings (20 out of 36 plots) and therefore statistical analysis of the data could not be carried out. However, the counts followed similar trends to those seen in Trial A and therefore these results are given in Tables 3 and 4. Table 3 shows the results of the counts on the main plot treatments. As in Trial A, the greatest number of seedlings occurred on the scarified plots followed by the burning treatment, rotovated plots having the least number of seedlings.

Again the sub-plots left bare (following main plot treatment) produced the greatest numbers of heather seedlings and spreading of capsules alone produced the least. Spreading of brashings and the sowing of capsules, together with a nurse grass, gave intermediate numbers of seedlings.

TABLE 3
Effects of scarification, rotovation and burning on the number of heather seedlings (seedling m^{-2})

Scarification	Rotovation	Burning
147	26	37

TABLE 4
Effects of sub-plot treatments on the number of heather seedlings
(seedlings m^{-2})

Spread brashings	Capsules + nurse grass	Spread capsules	Left bare
76	62	27	115

DISCUSSION
It is interesting to note the very marked difference with regard to the success of both experiments. Trial A was a relatively straightforward procedure involving the initial removal of the older heather material. Trial B did involve clearance of the above-ground, rather patchy heather plants, the surface grass sward and underlying thatch. The thatch was noted to form a layer of around 50 mm between the immediate surface and the underlying dark humus layer. Clearance of this thatch to expose the humus layer below may have inadvertently removed part of the humus, so reducing the available seed bank prior to the initiation of the sub-plot treatments.

During the assessment period a marked increase in the amount of coarse grass was noted in Trial B. This invasion was rapid, certain areas becoming completely overgrown in the period between application of the management treatments and the assessment.

The sub-plots receiving the burning treatment were, from visual inspection, most rapidly recolonised by coarse grass and this is possibly the main factor influencing the poor results obtained from burning in both trials.

From the data and information collated, a number of interesting points became apparent. In all cases the scarification (main plot) treatment gave the highest number of heather seedlings m^{-2}. This was greatest in those sub-plots left bare, i.e. without any further treatments. Germination of heather seed is known to require a light stimulus and this may be a major factor influencing the positive results obtained in those sub-plots left bare. All other sub-plot treatments resulted in the surface becoming covered, so reducing the light availability at the surface.

Although leaving the surface bare in this experiment, undertaken within a moderately high rainfall area, did prove most effective (average annual rainfall [1960-1988] 935 mm). Caution must be advised in the more southern, drier heathland sites where serious surface drying and possible erosion of a sandier surface may occur. Excessive sunlight may adversely affect seed germination and drought therefore will undoubtedly affect seedling survival.

It is interesting to note that in Trial A the sowing of a nurse grass with the spreading of capsules did result in significantly more heather seedlings than spreading either brashings or capsules alone. This further suggests that both capsules and brashings may in some instances smother the surface by their quantity which, combined with heavy rainfall, may suppress germination by the sheer weight of material lying on the surface. By contrast in dry heathland conditions, brashings and capsules may protect the surface, reducing moisture loss, thus avoiding germination and establishment of heather seedlings.

Although in both experiments the spreading of brashings gave a low rate of seedling establishment, other trials such as those conducted through British Gas (Anon. 1988) have resulted in relatively high rates of seedling establishment. The spreading of brashings in low rainfall areas, and in particular on the sandier soil types, may help indirectly by helping to reduce wind flow, thereby reducing evapotranspiratory losses and indeed sand blow from the surface.

On the more wet upland sites, scarification alone is aimed at clearing the above-ground material and creating small grooves through the surface may be sufficient to reinstate areas where either old and woody heather or patchy heather in and among coarser grass predominate.

Scarification
Scarification using suitable machinery is a valuable and useful technique in the reinstatement of a heather sward. This operation, by creating a number of small grooves through the surface, may indirectly help to protect the seed (having brought seed to the immediate surface) during its germination. Scarification will also clear the surface moss and debris, so opening the surface to light, thereby stimulating germination of the underlying seed bank.

Rotovation
Rotovation is an aggressive operation which physically overturns the surface, turning the soil through 100 mm (4 in.) depth. There may, therefore, be considerable dilution of available seed remaining at the surface following this operation.

Burning

Burning, in theory, is a viable and useful technique for heather restoration, but in practice there are many problems. If the heather is very dry and a large amount of plant material is present, the temperature of the burn is likely to become very hot, whilst if damp or wet the burn will be cool. Both extremes can severely affect the resulting regeneration.

If temperatures exceed 1,000°C all organic matter may be burnt off, this includes vegetative matter and seeds. If the burn is much below 400°C the burning may not chit the seeds, so reducing the germination stimulus. The main advantage of burning is that, if carried out correctly, it will burn off all debris and litter from the surface. With a cool burn the plant debris may not be cleared, restricting the available light reaching the surface. When the trial was first prepared and set up, there was a problem with the burning of the heather, primarily because the temperature could not be maintained above 400°C due to the prevailing climate.

Burning did not successfully remove the surface litter, woody stem material or the thatch which had accumulated and which may have been restricting light at the surface and therefore subsequent germination.

APPENDIX II

GREENKEEPER TRAINING

Greenkeeper's Training Committee (GTC)

This body is formed of representatives from the English, Irish, Scottish and Welsh Golf Unions, the Royal and Ancient Golf Club of St. Andrews, the British and International Golf Greenkeepers Association (BIGGA) and the Greenkeeping Associations of Ireland. The GTC has determined that golf greenkeepers are entitled to obtain a nationally recognised qualification for any formal training undertaken.

The GTC has also decided the training will not be restricted to the craft level only but will be in a format which enables greenkeepers to further their career prospects through a programme of learning throughout their career. The system allows greenkeepers at any stage in their career to enter or leave the system at a level appropriate to themselves.

The GTC wishes to encourage a productive partnership between employers, greenkeepers, trainees and training providers.

National/Scottish Vocational Qualifications (N/SVQs)

The introduction of these qualifications has meant a considerable shift in emphasis from the examination-based qualifications to a work-based learning and assessment system for competence. In practical terms this means that there must be much closer liaison between the training providers, golf clubs and course managers/head greenkeepers on behalf of the trainees.

The Training Manual

The GTC has developed a Greenkeeper's Training Manual as the main vehicle to guide and monitor the training of greenkeepers from a raw recruit up to course manager. The Manual is also designed to form a record of achievement for the trainee.

The Manual has three sections, craft, supervisory and management which complement N/SVQs at Levels 2, 3 and 4 respectively. Mandatory conservation units must also be completed at either the supervisory or management levels.

British and International Golf Greenkeepers Association

The British and International Golf Greenkeepers Association (BIGGA) has an influence on greenkeeper training policy by its membership of the GTC and the National Turfgrass Council (NTC). BIGGA has links with colleges, the Sports Turf Research Institute, the Institute of

Groundsmanship and European and world-wide greenkeeping associations. BIGGA has some 5,500 members in 31 different countries and is a major provider of greenkeeper education and training, attempting to identify areas of need not provided for elsewhere. BIGGA encourages greenkeepers to enter, participate and continue their education and training at all stages of their careers. The range, variety and location of BIGGA training courses, training videos, field guides and book/booklets continues to expand in order to improve the knowledge of greenkeepers, enhance their reputation and, consequently, improve the quality of golf courses.

DIRECTORY OF GTC APPROVED REGIONAL TRAINING COLLEGES

The following colleges are GTC "approved" to offer training courses at craft, supervisory and management levels.

England

Askham Bryan College – Askham Bryan, York, YO2 3PR. Contact Nick Bisset. Tel: 01904 702121.

Myerscough College – Myerscough hall, Bilsborrow, Preston, Lancashire, PR3 0RY. Contact Martyn Jones. Tel: 01995 640611.

Reaseheath College – Nantwich, Cheshire, CW5 6DF. Contact Dennis Mortram. Tel: 01270 625131.

Warwickshire College – Moreton Morrell, Warwick, CV35 9BL. Contact Chris Gray. Tel: 01926 651367.

Oaklands College – Oaklands Campus, Hatfield Road, St. Albans, Hertfordshire, AL4 0JA. Contact Ian Merrick. Tel: 01727 850651.

Plumpton College – Lewes, East Sussex, BN7 3AE. Contact David Blackmur. Tel: 01273 890454.

Cannington College – Cannington, Bridgwater, Somerset, TA5 2LS. Contact Nick Rigden. Tel: 01278 652226.

Sparsholt College – Sparsholt, Winchester, Hampshire, SO21 2NF. Contact Bob Young. Tel: 01962 776441.

Hadlow College of Agriculture and Horticulture – Hadlow, Tonbridge, Kent, TN11 0AL. Contact Keith Backhouse. Tel: 01732 850551

Wales

Welsh College of Horticulture – Northop, Mold, Clwyd, CH7 6AA. Contact G.M. Wright. Tel: 01352 86861. Fax: 01352 86731.

Scotland

Dundee College – Old Glamis Road, Dundee, DD3 8LE. Contact Graham Carr. Tel: 01382 819021. Fax: 01382 88117.

Elmwood College – Cupar, Fife, KY15 4JB. Contact Carol Borthwick. Tel: 01334 52781. Fax: 01334 56795.

Langside College – Glasgow School of Horticulture, Woodburn House, Buchanan Drive, Rutherglen, G73 3PF. Contact Colin S. Urquhart. Tel: 0141 647 6300.

Oatridge College – Ecclesmachan, Broxburn, West Lothian, EH52 6NH. Contact Steve Miller. Tel: 01506 854387.

Ireland
Teagasc College of Amenity Horticulture – National Botanic Gardens, Glasnevin, Dublin 9. Contact Pat Suttle. Tel: 00 3531 371636.

CRAFT LEVEL ONLY

Northern England
Durham College of Agriculture and Horticulture – Houghall, Durham, DH1 3SG. Contact Tony Milan. Tel: 0191 386 1351.

Midlands
Brooksby College – Brooksby, Melton Mowbray, Leicestershire, LE14 2LJ. Contact Paul Greene. Tel: 01664 434291.

South East
Writtle College – Chelmsford, Essex, CM1 3RR. Contact Dai Edwards. Tel: 01245 420705.

Otley College – Ipswich, Suffolk, IP6 9EY. Contact Stewart Brown. Tel: 01473 785543.

South West
Hartpury College – Hartpury House, Gloucester, GL19 3BF. Contact Andrew Laslo. Tel: 01452 700285.

Wales
Pencoed College – Pencoed, Mid Glamorgan, CF35 5LG. Contact Peter Gillard or Richard Browning. Tel: 01656 860202.

Scotland
Kyle and Carrick District Council – Burns House, Burns Statue Square, Ayr, KA7 1UT. Contact J. Dudgeon. Tel: 01292 281511.

Northern Ireland
Greenmount College of Agriculture and Horticulture – Antrim, BT41 4PU. Contact Geoff Jenkins. Tel: 018494 62114.

CRAFT AND SUPERVISORY LEVEL ONLY

North East Surrey College of Technology – Reigate Road, Ewell, Epsom, Surrey, KT17 3DS. Contact Dr. S. Shaw. Tel: 0181 394 3099/3111.

For more information please contact:

BIGGA, Aldwark Manor, Aldwark, Alne, York, North Yorkshire, YO6 2NF.

APPENDIX III

ABSTRACTION LICENSING AND WATER RESOURCES

It is the responsibility of the National Rivers Authority (NRA) to ensure that water resources are managed effectively and for the benefit of everyone. The NRA fulfils this role principally through the use of a system of water abstraction licensing. As a legal requirement under the Water Resources Act 1991, almost anyone who wants to take water from surface or underground source must obtain a licence to do so from the NRA.

The possession of a licence gives the abstractor a legal right to take water from the stated source every year until such time as the licence expires or the abstractor wishes to give up that right by cancelling the licence.

The licence will generally state how much water can be taken, when in the year water can be taken, what the water will be used for, the land where the water can be used, name and address of the licence abstractor, the duration of the licence, the source of supply, e.g. aquifer, river, etc., the means of abstraction, conditions the NRA stipulate in order to protect other interests on the water environment, the means by which abstraction is measured and records kept. Conditions can be placed on licences to protect the available water resources and ensure adequate flows and levels are available to maintain environmental stability. A common condition is that the abstraction must not result in the river flow being depleted below a pre-set or prescribed flow. At such times, further warnings may be issued to prevent further abstraction. If a licence is for the purpose of spray irrigation then there may be times, for example during a drought, when further restrictions are placed on abstraction. Indeed, under conditions of extreme water resource shortage, abstraction for spray irrigation may be banned altogether. Winter abstraction into storage lagoons would, however, normally be exempt from these restrictions.

Permission is required to carry out any work affecting a watercourse or the flow in it. This includes diversion of a watercourse, impounding water or constructing new drain headwalls or other structures on the banks of the watercourse.

Before undertaking any development, consultation should be made through one of the regional offices of the National Rivers Authority or, alternatively, through the Head Office, Rivers House, Waterside Drive, Aztec West, Almondsbury, Bristol, BS12 4UD, telephone 01454 624400.

REFERENCES AND FURTHER READING

I have below listed as essential a number of books worthy of special consultation by anyone seriously interested in applying ecological/ conservation principles and management techniques to golf and other additional references below.

Essential Reading

Anon. (1988). *Heathland Restoration : A Handbook of Techniques*. Environment Advisory Unit, University of Liverpool. Pub. by British Gas, Southampton, 160 pp.

Ash, H.J., Bennett, R. & Scott, R. (undated). *Flowers in the Grass*. English Nature, 68 pp.

Countryside Commission (1993). *Golf Courses in the Countryside*. Advisory Booklet, 48 pp.

Dair, I. and Schofield, J.M. (1990). Nature Conservation and the Management and Design of Golf Courses in Britain. In *Science and Golf. Proceedings of the First World Scientific Congress of Golf, 1990*, edited by A.J. Cochran. E. & F.N. Spon, London, pp. 330-335.

Emery, M. (1986). *Promoting Nature in Cities and Towns: A Practical Guide*. Croom Helm, 396 pp.

Hawtree, F.W. (1983). *The Golf Course: Planning, Design, Construction and Maintenance*. E. & F.N. Spon, London, 212 pp.

Hayes, P., Evans, R.D.C. & Isaac, S.P. eds. (1992). *The Care of the Golf Course*. The Sports Turf Res. Inst., Bingley, West Yorkshire, 266 pp.

Johnsons Seeds (1991). *Wild Flower Manual*. 38 pp.

Nature Conservancy Council (1988). *Site Management Plans for Nature Conservation: A Working Guide*., NCC, Peterborough, 40 pp.

Nature Conservancy Council (1990a). *Your Course – Preparing a Conservation Management Plan*. NCC, Peterborough, 15 pp.

Rodwell, J. & Patterson, G. (1994). Creating new native woodlands. *Forestry Authority Bulletin No. 112*, 78 pp.

Royal and Ancient Golf Club of St. Andrews (1989). *The Demand for Golf*. R&A Development Panel, St. Andrews, Scotland.

Royal and Ancient Golf Club of St. Andrews (1990). *The Way Forward*. R&A Greenkeeping Panel, St. Andrews, Scotland, 31 pp.

Schofield, M. & Dair, I. (Eds.) (1989). *On Course Conservation: Managing Golf's Natural Heritage*. Pub. by Nature Conservancy Council, Peterborough, 46 pp.

The Scottish Office Environmental Department (1994). *Golf Courses and Associated Developments*. Planning Advice Note PAN 43.

Thomas, E. & White, J.T. (1980). *Hedgerows*. Ash & Grant, 60 pp.

Additional References

Anon. (1983). *Wildlife on the Royal Birkdale.* Interpretive Branch, Nature Conservancy Council, Shrewsbury, 6 pp.

Anon. (1988). *A Strategy for Surrey Heathland.* Surrey County Council/ Nature Conservancy Council, Kingston-upon-Thames, 40 pp.

Anon. (1989). *Heather in England and Wales.* Institute of Terrestrial Ecology Res. Publ. No. 3 (Ed. R.G.H. Bunce), HMSO, London, 39 pp.

Anon. (1990). *Your Course – Preparing a Conservation Management Plan.* Nature Conservancy Council, Peterborough, 15 pp.

Anon. (1993). *Golf Courses – Friend or Foe of the Countryside.* British Assoc. of Nature Conservationists, Newbury, Berks., 72 pp.

Anon. (1994). *Golf's Natural Heritage.* Scottish Natural Heritage, 32 pp.

Anon. (1994). *Golf and the Environment.* United States Golf Assoc., NJ, USA, 20 pp.

Anon. (1994). *Golf Courses Benefit People and Wildlife.* United States Golf Assoc., NJ, USA, 4 pp.

Baldock, P.K.D. (1992). Environmental golf course management. *Golf Enterprise Europe*, May/June, pp. 20-22.

Balogh, J.C. & Walker, W.J. (Eds.) (1992). *Golf Course Management and Construction: Environmental Issues.* Lewis Publishers, Chelsea, MI, USA, 951 pp.

Beenstock, S. (1992). Going wild. *Turf Management*, February 1992, pp. 18-21.

Billion, F. (1992a). Golf in Germany. *Golf Enterprise Europe*, March 1992, pp. 18-22.

Billion, F. (1992b). The German experience. *Golf Enterprise Europe*, May/June 1992, pp. 31.

Binney, M. (1989). Inglorious golf courses. *Country Times and Landscape*, October 1989, pp 45.

Brennan, A. (1992). Do golf courses pollute the environment? *Golf Enterprise Europe*, May/June 1992, pp. 24-26.

Bunce, R.G.H. (Ed.) (1989). Heather in England & Wales. *Research Pub. No.3.* Institute of Terrestrial Ecology, HMSO, London, 40 pp. Council for the Protection of Rural England (1990). *Golf Courses – A Briefing Paper.* CPRE, London.

Countryside Commission (1991). *Environmental Assessment.* Technical Report, 52 pp.

Countryside Commission (1992). *New Golf Courses – Countryside Commission Policy.* CCP 365, January 1992, Cheltenham.

Dair, I. (1990). Conserving Golf and Wildlife. *Amateur Golf*, October 1990, pp. 30-31.

Department of the Environment (1991). *Planning Policy Guidance : Sport and Recreation.* DoE, PPG 17, September 1991, HMSO, London.

Department of the Environment (1992). *Environmental Assessment and Planning: Extension of Application*. DoE, Consultation paper. Planning and Development Control Division 4, June 1992.

Department of the Environment (1993). *The Potential for Woodland Establishment on Landfill Sites*. HMSO, 88 pp.

Dowdeswell, W.H (1987). *Hedgerows and Verges 1987*. Allen & Unwin, 160 pp.

English Heritage (1991). *Golf Course Proposals in Historic Landscapes*. English Heritage, London, 4 pp.

English Nature (1992). *Heather Condition and Management in the Uplands of England and Wales*, Peterborough, 51 pp.

Fisher, S. (1991). Wisley strikes a hole in one. *Horticulture Week*, 1 November 1991, pp. 26-29.

Fordham, M. (1988). Conservation management on golf courses. *J. Sports Turf Res. Inst.*, **64**, 10-18.

Fordham, M. & Iles, J. (1987). *Encouraging Wildlife on Golf Courses*. London Wildlife Trust, 12 pp.

Ghazi, P. & Lean, G. (1992). 'Greener' Britain after EC farm reform. *The Observer*, Sunday 24 May 1992, p. 3.

Gilchrist, T.D. (1983). *Trees on Golf Courses*. The Aboricultural Association, Romsey, Hampshire, 134 pp.

Gilpin, A. (1983). Golf course nature reserves. *Country Life*, 4 August 1983, pp. 282-283.

Glancey, J. (1991). Rough ride for a Rolls-Royce of golf courses. *The Independent*, 4 September 1991, p. 21.

Golf Course Wildlife Trust (undated). *Putting Wildlife and Golf Together*. Information Sheet. GCWT, London.

Green, B.H. & Marshall, I.C. (1987). An assessment of the role of golf courses in protecting and enhancing wildlife and landscapes. *Landscape and Urban Planning*, **14**, 143-154.

Grime, J.P., Hodgson, J.G. & Hunt, R. (1988). *Comparative Plant Ecology: A Functional Approach to Common British Species*. Unwin Hyman Ltd., London, 742 pp.

Harker, D., Evans, S., Evans, M. & Harker, K. (1993). *Landscape Restoration Handbook*. United States Golf Assoc., Lewis Publishers, Chelsea, MI. USA, 98 pp.

Heaton, C. (1992). Whole in one: an integrated systems approach to golf course design. *Golf Enterprise Europe*, May/June 1992, pp. 33-34.

Hillier, S.H., Walton, D.W.H. & Wells, D.A. (1990). *Calcareous Grasslands Ecology & Management*. NCC symposium, Bluntisham Books, 192 pp.

Lane, A. (1992). *Practical Conservation: Grasslands, Heaths and Moors*. Hodder & Stoughton, 128 pp.

Lawson, D.M. & Colclough, T.W. (1991). Fertiliser nitrogen, phosphorus and potassium leaching from fine turf growing on three different rootzone materials. *J. Sports Turf Res. Inst.*, **67**, 143-150.

Linde, D.T., Watschke, T.L. & Borger, J.A. (1994). Nutrient transport in run-off from two turfgrass species. In: *Science and Golf II. Proceedings of the World Scientific Congress of Golf.* Eds. Cochran & Farrally, E. & F.N. Spon, London, p. 639.

Linde, D.T., Watschke, T.L. & Borger, J.A. (1995). Transport of run-off and nutrients from fairway turf. *USGA Green Section Record* **33**, 1, 42-44.

Marshall, I. (1988). Wildlife in the rough. *Natural World*, Spring/ Summer 1988, pp. 14-17.

Miller, G.R., Miles, J. & Heal, O.W (1984). *Moorland Management : A Study of Exmoor.* Institute of Terrestrial Ecology/NERC, Cambridge, 118 pp.

Nature Conservancy Council (1984). *Nature Conservation in Britain.* NCC, Peterborough.

Nature Conservancy Council (1990b). *Handbook for Phase I Habitat Survey – a technique for environmental audit.* NCC, Peterborough, 78 pp.

North Berwick Study Group Report (1970). Dune conservation. *Study Conference Notes*, 44 pp.

Pearce, F. (1993). How green is your golf? *New Scientist*, 25 September, pp. 30-35.

Petrovic A.M. (1990). The fate of nitrogenous fertilizers applied to turfgrass. *Journal of Environmental Quality*, **19**, 1-14.

Petrovic, A.M. (1994). Impact of golf courses on ground water quality. In: *Science and Golf II. Proceedings of the World Scientific Congress of Golf.* Eds. Cochran & Farrally, E. & F.N. Spon, London, p. 639.

Petrovic, A.M. (1995). The impact of soil type and precipitation on pesticide and nutrient leaching from fairway turf. *USGA Green Section Record* **33**, 1, 38-41.

Picksley, K. (1988). *A Strategy for Surrey Heathland.* Surrey County Council and The Nature Conservancy Council, Kingston-on-Thames, 40 pp.

Rackham, O. (1989). *The History of the Countryside*, 445 pp.

Rorison, I.H. & Hunt, R. (1980). *Amenity Grassland: An Ecological Perspective.* Wiley & Sons, Chichester, 261 pp.

Russell, G. (1992b). When it's green to be brown. *Golf Enterprise Europe*, May/June 1992, p. 4.

Russell, G. (1992c). A European golf environmental policy. *Golf Enterprise Europe*, May/June 1992, p. 32.

Shildrick, J.P. (Ed.) (1984). Creating attractive grasslands. *Workshop Report No.5.* National Turfgrass Council, Bingley, W. Yorks., 92 pp.

Shildrick, J.P. (Ed.) (1988). Wild flowers '87. *Workshop Report No.14.* National Turfgrass Council, Bingley, W. Yorks., 90 pp.

Stubbs, D. & Hare, T. (1985). Wildlife links – flora and fauna of London's golf courses. *Country Life*, 14 November 1985, pp. 1513-1514.

Tait, J., Lane, A. & Carr, S. (1988). *Practical Conservation - Site Assessment and Management Planning.* Open University.

Tarling, J. (1992). Golf course development – is there a need for environmental assessment? *Golf Enterprise Europe*, May/June 1992, pp. 29-30.

Taylor, R.S. (1990). Conservation and ecological management on the golf course. *Sports Turf Bulletin*, **169**, April-June 1990, pp. 9-11.

Taylor, R.S. (1991). Ecology and the greenkeeper. *Greenkeeper International*, November 1991, pp. 8-9.

Taylor, R.S., Stefanyszyn, O. & Canaway, P.M (1994). Reinstatement of heather on the golf course using physical and mechanical methods. *J. Sports Turf Res. Inst.* **70**, 7-12.

Tomlinson, D. (1991). Keeping golf green. *Country Life*, 31 January 1991, pp. 42-43.

Vidal, J. (1992). One more manicure for Mother Nature. *The Guardian*, 17 July 1992, p. 27.

Viney, L. & Gallacher, B. eds. (1989). *Benson and Hedges Golfers Handbook.* Macmillan Press Limited, London, 890 pp.

Willcox, A. (1992). Golf course design. *Golf Club Management*, April 1992, p. 20.

Windsor & Maidenhead Urban Wildlife Group (1992). *Wildlife at Temple Golf Club.* Survey Report, 45 pp.

White, D. (1991). The ocean course. *Greenkeeper International*, January/February 1991, pp. 18-21.

The British and International Golf Greenkeepers Association would like to thank the following Golden and Silver Key members for their contributions to the BIGGA Education and Development Fund which provided the funding for this publication.

GOLDEN AND SILVER KEY MEMBERS

Amenity Technology
Avoncrop Amenity Products
E.T. Breakwell Ltd.
Fenchurch Insurance Brokers Ltd.
Hardi Ltd.
Hayter Ltd.
Jacobsen Division of Textron Ltd.
Kubota (UK) Ltd.
Lely (UK) Ltd.
Massey Ferguson Grass Equipment
Miracle Amenity Care (formerly Zeneca/ICI Professional Products)
Ransomes Sims & Jefferies Ltd.
Rhone-Poulenc Environmental Products
Rigby Taylor Ltd.
Risboro' Turf
Sisis Equipment (Macclesfield) Ltd.
The Toro Company